INSTRUCTOR'S MODULE 5
THE NERVOUS SYSTEM

ELAINE N. MARIEB
Holyoke Community College

AND

PETER ZAO
North Idaho College

To Accompany
Human Anatomy and Physiology, Second Edition
by Elaine N. Marieb

D1372102

The Benjamin/Cummings Publishing Company, Inc.
Redwood City, California • Menlo Park, California
Reading, Massachusetts • New York • Don Mills, Ontario
Wokingham, U.K. • Amsterdam • Bonn • Sydney
Singapore • Tokyo • Madrid • San Juan

ISBN 0-8053-4133-1

1 2 3 4 5 6 7 8 9 10 - AL - 95 94 93 92 91

The Benjamin/Cummings Publishing Company, Inc.
390 Bridge Parkway
Redwood City, California 94065

Fundamentals of the Nervous System and Nervous Tissue

11

CHAPTER PREVIEW

This chapter begins with a brief overview of the organization of the nervous system. It then focuses on the functional anatomy of nervous tissue, especially that of the nerve cells, or neurons, that are the key to the subtle, efficient system of neural communication. The histology and neurophysiology of the tissue is presented and explained in detail. Concepts of neural integration, patterns of neural organization, the reflex arc, and the developmental aspects of the nervous tissue are also described.

AT A GLANCE

INTEGRATING THE PACKAGE

SUGGESTED LECTURE OUTLINE

I. Introduction (pp.340-341)
    A. Basic Characteristics (p. 340)
    B. Functions (pp. 340-341
        1. Monitors Changes

        2. Integration
        3. Effects Responses

II. Organization of the Nervous System (pp. 341-342; Fig. 11.1, p. 341)
        A. Central Nervous System (p. 341)
        B. Peripheral Nervous System (pp. 341-342)
            1. Afferent (Sensory) Division
            2. Efferent (Motor) Division
                a. Somatic Nervous System
                b. Automatic Nervous System
                    1. Sympathetic Division
                    2. Parasympathetic Division

III. Histology of Nervous Tissue (pp. 342-350)
        A. Supporting Cells (pp. 342-343; Fig. 11.2, p. 343)
            1. Basic Characteristics
            2. Neuroglia
                a. Astrocytes
                b. Microglia
                c. Ependymal
                d. Oligodendrocytes
                e. Schwann Cells
                f. Satellite Cells
        B. Neurons (pp. 343-350)
            1. Basic Characteristics (Fig. 11.3, p. 344)
            2. Neuron Cell Body
                a. Perikaryon
                b. Nissl Bodies
                c. Neurofilaments
                d. Pigment Inclusions
            3. Nuclei
            4. Ganglia
            5. Neuron Processes
                a. Tracts
                b. Nerves
                c. Dendrites
                d. Axons
                    1. Axon Hillock
                    2. Axoplasm
                    3. Axon Collaterals
                    4. Telodendria
                    5. Axonal Terminals
                    6. Axonal Transport
                    7. Axoplasmic Flow
                    8. Myelin Sheath (Fig. 11.4, p. 347)
                        a. Myelinated Fibers
                        b. Unmyelinated Fibers
                        c. Schwann Cells
                        d. Neurilemma
                        e. Nodes of Ranvier
                        f. White Matter
                        g. Gray Matter
        C. Classification of Neurons (pp. 346-350)
            1. Structural Classification (Fig. 11.5, p. 346)

REVIEW ITEMS

---

5. Cell cycle (Chapter 3, p. 88)

6. Enzymes and enzyme function (Chapter 2, p. 53)

7. Synapse (neuromuscular junction) (Chapter 9, p. 258-259)

8. Membrane proteins (transport) (Chapter 3, p. 69)

CROSS-REFERENCES

---

1. Cholinergic and adrenergic receptors and other neurotransmitter effects are described in Chapter 14, pp. 467-468.

2. Receptors for the special senses are presented in Chapter 16.

3. Nervous system modulation of endocrine function is examined in Chapter 17, p. 547.

4. Membrane potential and the electrical activity of the heart is explained in great detail in Chapter 19, 614-620.

5. Examples of receptors are given in Chapter 25, p. 864.

6. Sensory receptors and control of digestive processes are described in Chapter 24.

7. Chemoreceptors and stretch receptors related to respiratory function are covered in Chapter 23, pp. 756-759.

8. Baroreceptors and chemoreceptors in blood pressure and flow regulation regulation are examined in Chapter 20, pp. 640-643.

9. Synapses involved in the special senses are examined in Chapter 16.

10. Neurotransmitters in the special senses are further described in Chapter 16.

11. Neural integration is presented in great detail in Chapters 13, p. 448; 14, pp. 471-471; and 15, pp. 476-485.

12. Membrane potentials are further described in Chapter 13, pp. 425-426.

13. Autonomic synapses are presented in Chapters 13, p 430; 14, p. 466-468.

14. Cutaneous sensory receptors (Chapter 13, p. 425)

ANSWERS TO TEXTBOOK CHAPTER QUESTIONS

Multiple Choice/Matching

1. b

2. (1)d; (2)b; (3)f; (4)c; (5)a

7. b

8. d

3. b   9. c

4. c   10.

5. a   11. a

6. c   12. (1)d; (2)b; (3)a; (4)c

Short Answer Essay Questions

13. Anatomical division includes the CNS (brain and spinal cord) and the PNS (nerves and ganglia). Functional division includes the somatic and autonomic motor divisions of the PNS. The autonomic division is divided into sympathetic and parasympathetic subdivisions. (pp.341-342)

14. a. The cell body is the biosynthetic and metabolic center of a neuron. It contains the usual organelles, but lacks centrioles. (pp. 344-345)
    b. Dendrites and axons both function to carry electrical current. Dendrites differ in that they are short, transmit toward the cell body, and function as receptor sites. Axons are typically long, are myelinated, and transmit away from the cell body. (p. 345)

15. a. Myelin is a whitish, fatty, phospholipid insulating material (essentially the wrapped plasma membranes of oligodendrocytes or Schwann cells).
    b. CNS myelin sheaths are formed by flap-like extensions of oligodendrocytes and lack a neurilemma. Fibers cannot regenerate. PNS myelin is formed by Schwann cells. The sheaths have a neurilemma, and the fibers they protect are capable of regeneration. (p. 346)

16. Multipolar neurons have many dendrites, one axon, and are found in the CNS (and autonomic ganglia). Bipolar neurons have one axon and one dendrite, and are found in receptor end organs of the special senses such as the retina of the eye and olfactory mucosa. Unipolar neurons have one process that divides into an axon and a dendrite and is a sensory neuron with the cell body found in a dorsal root ganglion or cranial nerve ganglion. (pp. 346-349)

17. A polarized membrane possesses a net positive charge outside, and a net negative charge inside, with the voltage across the membrane being at -70 mv. Diffusion of Na^+ and K^+ across the membrane establishes the resting potential because the membrane is slightly more permeable to K^+. The Na^+-K^+ pump, an active transport mechanism, maintains this polarized state by maintaining the diffusion gradient for Na^+ and K^+. (pp. 351-352; see Fig. 11.7, p. 352)

18. a. The generation of an action potential involves: (1) an increase in sodium permeability and reversal of the membrane potential; (2) a decrease in sodium permeability; and (3) an increase in potassium permeability and repolarization. (Fig. 11.11, p. 355)
    b. The ionic gates are controlled by changes in the membrane potential and activated by local currents. (p. 355)
    c. The all-or-none phenomenon means that the local depolarizing current must reach a critical "firing" or threshold point before it will respond, and when it responds, it will respond completely by conducting the action potential along the entire length of its axon. (p. 357)

19. The CNS "knows" a stimulus is strong when the frequency or rate of action potential generation is high. (p. 358)

20. a. An EPSP is an excitatory (depolarizing) postsynaptic potential that increases the chance of a depolarization event. An IPSP is an inhibitory (hyperpolarizing) postsynaptic potential that decreases the chance of a depolarization event. (See Table 11.2, p. 363)

b. It is determined by the type of neurotransmitter that binds at the postsynaptic neuron and the specific receptor subtype it binds to. (p. 362)

21. Each neuron's axon hillock keeps a "running account" of all signals it receives via temporal and spatial summation. (p. 364)

22. The neurotransmitter is quickly removed by enzymatic degradation or reuptake into the presynaptic axon. This insures discrete limited responses. (p. 362)

23. a. Absolute refractory period is when the neuron is incapable of responding to another stimulus because repolarization is still occurring. (p. 358)
    b. A-fibers have the largest diameter and thick myelin sheaths and conduct impulses quickly; B-fibers are lightly myelinated, have intermediate diameters, and are slower conductors. (p. 359)
    c. Node of Ranvier is an interruption of the myelin sheath due to wrapping of the individual Schwann cells. (p. 346)

24. In serial processing the pathway is constant and through a definite sequence of neurons. In parallel processing, impulses reach the final CNS target by multiple pathways. Parallel processing allows for a variety of response. (p. 372)

25. First, they proliferate; second, they migrate to proper position; third, they differentiate. (p. 373)

26. Factors include "pathfinder" neurons; orienting glial fibers; and attracting substances such as nerve cell adhesion molecules and growth cones. (p. 373)

Critical Thinking and Application Questions

1. The resting potential would decrease, that is, become less negative, because the concentration gradient causing net diffusion of K^+ out of the cell would be smaller. Action potentials would be fired more easily, that is, in response to smaller stimuli, because the resting potential would be closer to threshold. Repolarization would occur more slowly because repolarization depends on net K^+ diffusion from the cell and the concentration gradient driving this diffusion is lower. Also, the after hyperpolarization would be smaller. (pp. 354-356)

2. Local anesthetics such as novocaine and sedatives affect the neural processes usually at the nodes of Ranvier, by reducing the membrane permeability to sodium ions. (p. 359)

3. The bacteria remain in the wound, however, the toxin produced travels via axonal transport to reach the cell body. (p. 346)

LABORATORY CORRELATIONS

1. Marieb, E. N. <u>Human Anatomy and Physiology Laboratory Manual: Cat and Fetal Pig Versions</u>. 3rd. ed. Benjamin/Cummings, 1989.

    Exercise 17: Histology of Nervous Tissue
    Exercise 20: Neurophysiology of Nerve Impulses

2. Marieb, E. N. <u>Human Anatomy and Physiology Laboratory Manual; Brief Version</u>. 3rd. ed. Benjamin/Cummings, 1992.

Exercise 15: Neuron Anatomy and the Nerve Impulse

OVERHEAD TRANSPARENCIES INDEX

Transparency	Description
11.2	Supporting cells of nervous tissue
11.3	Structure of a Motor Neuron
11.4	Relation of Schwann cells to axons in PNS
11.7	Passive and active forces that establish and maintain the resting membrane potential
11.12	The Hodgkin cycle
11.13	Propagation of an action potential
11.17	Events occuring at a chemical synapse
11.22	Mechanism of a metabotropic neurotransmitter
11.25	Simple reflex arcs

BLACK LINE MASTER INDEX

Black Line Master	Description
11.2	Supporting cells of nervous tissue
11.3	Structure of a Motor Neuron
11.4	Relation of Schwann cells to axons in PNS
11.12	The Hodgkin cycle
11.17	Events occuring at a chemical synapse
11.25	Simple reflex arcs

INSTRUCTIONAL AIDS

LECTURE HINTS

1. By this time, the class has been exposed to only a few systems (integumentary, skeletal, and muscular) but enough information has been given so that students can understand the basics of nervous system function from the beginning of this section. Ask students questions, e.g.: (1) When you touch something hot, how do you react? (2) Do you have to consciously think about pulling your hand away? The idea for these basic, probing questions is to get students to come up with the idea that a neural pathway consists of a sensory structure, some means of conveying information to the brain, and some means of causing motor response. If you get students to come up with these "solutions," they will remember the logic used to derive the answers.

2. Emphasize strongly the three basic functions of the nervous system: sensory, integration, and motor. Students should "burn this into the brain," since it will be seen again and again in all systems.

3. Stress that although we discuss the nervous system in segments, it is actually tightly integrated.

4. Present a general introduction of the entire nervous system near the beginning of nervous system discussion so that students will be able to see the entire "picture." In this way, they will better understand the relationships as material is covered.

5. Point out the similarities between skeletal muscle cells and neurons. It is also possible to introduce the electrical characteristics of cardiac pacemaker cells (modified muscle cells) and note the similarities to neuron function. It is worthwhile to point out that although function is totally different, (muscle=contractile, nervous=impulse generation,propagation) structural basis of each is a slight modification of a basic cellular blueprint.

6. Bring a model (or overheads, 2X2 slides) of a neuron to lecture to visually demonstrate the anatomy of a nerve cell.

7. Many students have difficulty understanding the difference between the myelin sheath and the neurilemma (sheath of Schwann). Use a diagram (black line master) to point out that both are parts of the same cell.

8. Emphasize the difference in myelination between the CNS and PNS. Point out the regeneration capabilities of each.

9. Many students have trouble relating ion movements with electrical current. One way to approach neurophysiology is to (loosly) compare a 1.5V battery to the cell membrane (something students can relate to). The electrical potential between the positive and negative poles is analogous to the outside and inside of a cell. When a connection is made between positive and negative poles (ion gates opened) current is delivered.

10. Clearly distinguish the difference between graded potentials and action potentials. It helps to use a full page acetate of a neuron to demonstrate the positive feedback nature of the action potential.

11. Most inroductory physiology students will experience difficulty with the idea of saltatory conduction. Draw (or project) disgrams of myelinated vs. unmyelinated fibers and electrical propagation.

12. Do a diagram of a synapse, then use root word dissection to emphasize the distinction between pre- and postsynaptic neurons. This is a good introduction to the synapse, and establishes a reference point upon which students can build.

13. Use absolute numbers as an introductory example for summation, for example: If three presynaptic neurons each simultaneously deliver a one-third threshold stimulus, will the postsynaptic neuron fire? Use several examples to emphasize the difference between spatial and temporal summation.

14. Use diagrams when describing the different types if circiuts.

DEMONSTRATIONS/ACTIVITIES

1. Film(s) or other audiovisual materials of choice.

2. Obtain a microprojector and microscope slides of neurons, neuroglia, and peripheral nerves to illustrate the histology of the tissue.

3. Obtain an oscilloscope and a neurophysiology kit to illustrate how an action potential can be registered.

4. Obtain 3-D models of motor and sensory neurons to illustrate their similarities and differences.

5. To illustrate proprioception, have students place their hands at their sides and then, without allowing them to look, have them visualize where the backs of their hands are.

6. Use a match to illustrate how an EPSP can work and how a graded potential will be intense at the receptor end and decrease thereafter; then use a fuse wire to illustrate how an action potential is carried down the wire.

CRITICAL THINKING/DISCUSSION TOPICS

1. How can drugs, such as novocaine, effectively block the transmission of pain impulses? Why don't they block motor impulses, or do they?

2. What effect does alcohol have on the transmission of electrical impulses?

3. How can rubbing one's nose decrease the possibility of a sneeze? Discuss in terms of EPSP's an IPSP's.

4. Acetylcholine has long been recognized as a neurotrans- mitter. Why has it been so difficult to identify other neurotransmitters?

5. How can some people eat extremely "hot" peppers without experiencing the same pain that others normally have?

6. What would happen at the synapse if one introduced an agent that blocked the activity of chemically gated Na^+ channels? K^+ channels?

LIBRARY RESEARCH TOPICS

1. Of what value is the development of recombinant DNA technology to our study of protein-based neurotransmitters?

2. What is the status of research on the repair and/or regeneration of nervous tissue of the CNS?

3. Why do most tumors of nervous tissue develop in neuroglia rather than neurons?

4. Could we use neurotransmitters to enhance our memory capacity?

5. How are experiments performed to test the anatomy and physiology of plasma membrane ion gates and channels?

AUDIO VISUAL AIDS/COMPUTER SOFTWARE

Films

1. The Ionic Basis of the Action Potential (USNAC, 11 min., C, 1977). Uses computer animation to illustrate the dynamic relationship of three molecular events: channel activity, ion movement, and charge separation.

2. The Nerve Impulse (EBE, 21 min., C, 1971). History of discoveries of nerve impulse properties. Physiology of the nervous system.

Filmstrips/Slides

1. The Nervous System - Unit 5 (CA, RB-368, Filmstrip)

2. Histology of the Nervous System (EI, #613, Slides) Various stain techniques used to show cell bodies, myelin sheath, neurons, and glial cells.

3. Nervous System and Its Function (EI, SS-0350F, Filmstrips or Slides) Reviews neural transmission, brain areas, and spinal cord.

4. Neurobiology I: Excitatory Membranes (EI, EP-2138, 1984, Slides) Describes resting membrane potential, action potential, and active transport mechanisms.

5. Neurobiology II: Neural Function (EI, EP-2139, 1984, Slides) Describes information processing, EPSP's and IPSP's.

6. Nervous System: Structure and Function (WNSE, 78 W 0610)

Videotapes

1. Nerves at Work (FHS, QB-831, 26 min., C, VHS/BETA) Program explores nerve signals, impulse transmission, and reflex activities. Also available in 16 mm.

2. Decision (FHS, QB-832, 26 min., C, VHS/BETA) Program shows how the brain organizes input and output, and how circuits of nerve cells operate. Also available in 16 mm.

3. Brain Triggers, Part 1 - Neurotransmitters (PLP, CH-770234, VHS)

4. Your Body - Part 3, Your Nervous System. (PLP, CH-140203, VHS)

Computer Software

1. The Nervous System: Our Information Network (CA, MLC 5131, Apple)

2. Dynamics of the Human Nervous System (EI, C-3050, Apple/IBM)

3. Nervous System (PLP, CH-381079, Apple 64K)

4. Body Language: Study of Human Anatomy, Nervous System (PLP, CH-182013, Apple; CH-182014, IBM)

5. The Human Systems:Series 2 (PLP, CH-920009, Apple)

6. The Human Brain (PLP, CH-510003, Apple)

See *Guide to Audiovisual Resources* at the end of this module for key to AV distributors

LECTURE ENHANCEMENT MATERIAL

CLINICAL AND RELATED TERMS

1. Ependymitis - inflammation of the membrane lining the cerebral ventricles.

2. Ganglionitis - inflammation of a ganglion.

3. Synaptic Plasticity - the ability of the synapse to change at both the molecular and at the cellular level.

DISORDERS/HOMEOSTATIC IMBALANCES

Demyelinating Disorders

1. Tay-Sach's Disease - an inherited infantile form of amaurotic familial idiocy marked by degeneration of brain tissue due to an inborn error in metabolism. A deficiency of the enzyme, hexosaminidase A, results in a sphingolipodosis with an accumulation of GM2 gangliosides in the brain.

2. Post-Infectious Encephalomyelitis - a rapidly occurring demyelination of the nerve tissue that may follow diseases such as measles, vaccinia, encephalitis, etc.

Motor Neuron Disorders

1. Amyotrophic Lateral Sclerosis (ALS) - a progressive neurologic disorder characterized by degeneration of lower motor neuron cell bodies in the gray matter of the anterior horns of the spinal cord, brain, and pyramidal tracts. It is also called motor neuron disease and "Lou Gehrig's disease." There is no known cause or cure.

2. Wernig-Hoffman Disease - an inherited infantile motor neuron disease exhibiting type I spinal muscular atrophy.

Disorders on Neuroglial Cells

1. Astrocytoma - a usually slow-growing neoplasm derived from astrocytes. Classified in order of malignancy as: Grade I, consisting of fibrillary or protoplasmic astrocytes; Grade II, astroblastoma; and, Grades III and IV, glioblastoma multiforme.

2. Ependymoma - a slow-growing neoplasm derived from ependymal cells that line the ventricles of the brain and form the central canal of the spinal cord. Prognosis is extremely poor.

3. Glioblastoma Multiforme - an astrocytoma of Grade III or IV; usually rapid-growing and occurring in the cerebral hemispheres; composed of spongioblasts, astroblasts, and astrocytes. Prognosis is generally very poor.

4. Glioneuroma - a glioma combined with neuroma.

5. Oligodendroglioma - a neoplasm derived from and composed of oligodendroglia. They are among the most unpredictable gliomas and are capable of rapid progression.

6. Schwannoma - a neoplasm originating from Schwann cells that form the myelin sheath of neurons. These tumors include neurofibromas and neurilemomas.

APPLIED PHARMACOLOGY

Poisons Affecting the Nervous System

1. Alpha - Bungarotoxin - a highly potent toxin derived from the venom of Bungarus snakes that binds to ACh receptor proteins.

2. Diisopropyl Fluorophosphate (DFP) - a highly toxic insecticide and nerve gas that irreversibly inactivates acetylcholinesterase. An early compound, parathion, became employed as a popular insecticide. Still others, Sarin, Soman, and Tabun, were developed by the Germans during WWII for use as highly toxic nerve gases.

3. Physostigmine (Eserine) - an alkaloid obtained from the calabar bean of the plant, Physostigma venenosum. Acts as a reversible anticholinesterase agent. Once used by African tribes as an "ordeal poison" for witchcraft.

4. Saxitoxin - a shellfish (Gonyaulax) poison produced by unicellular organisms that cause the red tide. The paralysis associated with the toxin is due to blockage of chemically regulated sodium gates.

5. Tetrodotoxin - a highly toxic substance derived from a puffer fish that blocks sodium channels. May cause death by paralysis of respiratory muscles.

Narcotic Analgesics

1. Morphine - A narcotic that produces euphoria by attaching to natural enkephalin receptors.

2. Codeine and Codeine Congeners - used in the relief of mild-to-moderate pain and cough. Mimics endogenous opioid peptides such as the endorphins and enkephalins. Act as agonists at the opiate receptors in the spinal cord and CNS.

3. Synthetic and Semisynthetic Agonists (Meperidine, Fentanyl, Alphaprodine) - act similar to morphine in providing relief to moderate and severe pain. Used as a preoperative medication, supplement to anesthesia, and for obstetrical analgesia.

4. Methadone - used for severe pain, narcotic detoxification, and in the maintenance treatment for narcotic addiction. Acts as an opiate agonist that is well-absorbed by the GI tract.

5. Mixed Opiate Agonist - Antagonists (Butorphanol, Penta- zocine) - used for relief of moderate-to-severe pain for preoperative medication and anesthetic supplement in obstetrical anesthesia. Provides effective analgesia but does not develop tolerance as readily as pure agonists. Acts as kappa and sigma receptor agonists and mu receptor antagonists.

6. Antagonists (Naloxone, Levallorphan) - used for respiratory depression caused by narcotic analgesics. Acts as a pure opiate antagonist but is not effective in patients not receiving opiates. Antagonist to delta, kappa, and mu opiate receptor sites.

SUGGESTED READINGS

1. Adams, R.V. Principles of Neurology. 2nd ed. New York:McGraw-Hill, 1981.

2. Bainbridge, Jr., J.S. "Frogs That Sweat-Not Bullets, But a Poison for Darts." Smithsonian 19 (Jan. 1089):70-76.

3. Bloom, F. "Brain Drugs." Science 85 (Nov. 1985):100-101.

4. Bloom, F.E. "Neuropeptides." Scientific American 245 (Oct. 1981).

5. Carpenter, M.B. Human Neuroanatomy. 7th ed. Baltimore: Williams and Wilkins, 1976.

6. Catterall, W.A. "The Molecular Basis of Neuronal Excitability." Science 223 (1984):653.

7. Dunant, Y., and M. Israel. "The Release of Acetylcholine." Scientific American 252 (Apr. 1985):58-66.

8. Hodgkin, A.L. "The Ionic Basis of Nervous Conduction." Science 145 (Sept. 1964).

9. Goodman, C.S. and M.J. Bastiani "How Embryonic Cells Recognize One Another." Scientific American, (Dec. 1984):58-66.

10. Gottlieb, D.I. "GABAergic Neurons." Scientific American 258 (Feb. 1988):82-89.

11. Kalil, R.E. "Synapse Formation in the Developing Brain." Scientific American 261 (Dec. 1989):76-85.

12. Kandel, E.R. "Small Systems of Neurons." Scientific American (Sept. 1979).

13. Keynes, R.D. "Ion Channels in the Nerve Cell Membrane." Scientific American (Sept. 1979).

14. Kimelberg, H.K. and M.D. Norenberg "Astrocytes." Scientific American 260 (Apr. 1989):66-76.

15. Kuffler, S.W., et al. From Neuron to Brain: A Cellular Approach to Function of the Nervous System. Sunderland, MA:Sinauer, 1984.

16. Lester, H.A. "The Response to Acetylcholine." Scientific American (Feb. 1977).

17. Levi-Montalcini, R., and P. Calissano. "The Nerve Growth Factor." Scientific American 240 (June 1979):68-77.

18. Llinas, R.R. "Calcium in Synaptic Transmission." Scientific American 247 (Oct. 1982).

19. McGeer, P.L. "The Chemistry of the Mind." American Scientist 59 (Mar.-Apr. 1971).

20. Miller, J.A. "Grow, Nerves, Grow." Science News 129 (Mar. 1986):204-206.

21. Morell, P., and W.T. Norton. "Myelin." Scientific American (May 1980).

22. Nauta, W.J.H., and M. Feirtag. Fundamental Neuroanatomy. New York:W.H. Freeman and Co., 1985.

23. Patterson, P.H., et al. "The Chemical Differentiation of Nerve Cells." Scientific American 239 (July 1978):50-59.

24. Schwartz, J.H. "The Transport of Substances in Nerve Cells." Scientific American (Apr. 1980).

25. Shepherd, G.M. "Microcircuits in the Nervous System." Scientific American (Feb. 1978).

26. Snyder, S.H. "Opiate Receptors and Internal Opiates." Scientific American 236 (Mar. 1977):44-56.

27. Stevens, C.F. "The Neuron." Scientific American 241 (Sept. 1979):54-65.

28. Wurtman, R.J. "Nutrients That Modify Brain Function." Scientific American 246 (Apr. 1982):50-59.

HANDOUTS

The following section contains prepared handout material which may be photocopied and distributed to the class. All materials are organized so that selected items can be cut and pasted for the instructors individual needs.

If budgets are a limiting factor in the use of handouts, these masters may be placed on reserve in the library for students to photocopy at their convenience.

Preview Of Selected Key Terms

Central nervous system (CNS) . . . . The brain and spinal cord.

Peripheral nervous system (PNS) . . . . . . All nervous system structures outside of the CNS; i.e., nerves, ganglia, and sensory receptors.

Neuroglia . . . . (neuro=nerve; glia=glue) Nonexcitable cells of neural tissue that support, protect, and insulate the neurons.

Neuron . . . . Cell of the nervous system specialized to generate and transmit nerve impulses

Dendrite . . . . (dendr=tree) Branching neuron process that serves as a receptive, or input, region.

Axon . . . . (axo=axis, axle) Neuron process that conducts impulses.

Myelin sheath . . . . Fatty insulating sheath that surrounds all but the emallest nerve fibers.

Sensory receptor . . . . Dendritic end organs, or parts of other cell types, specialized to respond to a stimulus.

Graded potential . . . . A local change in membrane potential that declines with distance and is not conducted along the nerve fiber.

Action potential . . . . A large transient depolarization event, including polarity reversal, that is conducted along the nerve fiber; also called the nerve impulse.

Saltatory conduction . . . . Transmission of an action potential along a myelinated fiber in which the nerve impulse appears to leap from node to node.

Synapse . . . . (synaps= a union) Functional junction or point of close contact between two neurons or between a neuron and an effector cell.

Neurotransmitter . . . . Chemical substance released by neurons that may, upon binding to receptors of neurons or effector cells, stimulate or inhibit those cells.

Sensory transduction . . . . Conversion of stimulus energy into a nerve impulse.

Terms/Disorders

1. Alpha - Bungarotoxin - a highly potent toxin derived from the venom of Bungarus snakes that binds to ACh receptor proteins.

2. Amyotrophic Lateral Sclerosis (ALS) - a progressive neurologic disorder characterized by degeneration of lower motor neuron cell bodies in the gray matter of the anterior horns of the spinal cord, brain, and pyramidal tracts. It is also called motor neuron disease and "Lou Gehrig's disease." There is no known cause or cure.

3. Codeine and Codeine Congeners - used in the relief of mild-to-moderate pain and cough. Mimics endogenous opioid peptides such as the endorphins and enkephalins. Act as agonists at the opiate receptors in the spinal cord and CNS.

4. Ependymitis - inflammation of the membrane lining the cerebral ventricles.

5. Ganglionitis - inflammation of a ganglion.

6. Methadone - used for severe pain, narcotic detoxification, and in the maintenance treatment for narcotic addiction. Acts as an opiate agonist that is well-absorbed by the GI tract.

7. Morphine - A narcotic that produces euphoria by attaching to natural enkephalin receptors.

8. Post-Infectious Encephalomyelitis - a rapidly occurring demyelination of the nerve tissue that may follow diseases such as measles, vaccinia, encephalitis, etc.

9. Saxitoxin - a shellfish (Gonyaulax) poison produced by unicellular organisms that cause the red tide. The paralysis associated with the toxin is due to blockage of chemically regulated sodium gates.

10. Tay-Sach's Disease - an inherited infantile form of amaurotic familial idiocy marked by degeneration of brain tissue due to an inborn error in metabolism. A deficiency of the enzyme, hexosaminidase A, results in a sphingolipodosis with an accumulation of GM2 gangliosides in the brain.

11. Tetrodotoxin - a highly toxic substance derived from a puffer fish that blocks sodium channels. May cause death by paralysis of respiratory muscles.

Age Associated Changes

Gross Morphological Changes

        -Decrease in the number of neurons
        -Decreased brain weight
        -Decreased brain size
        -Decreased mass of the gyri
        -Fibrosis of the meninges
        -Increased size of the sulci
        -Increased size of the subarachmoid space
        -Increased size of the ventricles

Cellular Changes

        -Increased lipofuscin deposition
        -Increased presence of neurofibrillary tangles
        -Decreased number of synaptic junctions
        -Increased areas of nervous tissue degeneration (senile plaques)
        -Altered neurotransmitter function

Functional Alterations

        -Reflex action decreases
        -Ankle reflex is usually first lost
        -Infancy reflexes reappear (e.g., sucking)
        -Loss of muscle mass due to decreased neural function
        -Decreased efficiency of vision control
        -Decreased smell and taste sensation
        -Decreased efficiency of motor control

The following section contains selected unlabeled line art representations of key elements in this chapter. These diagrams may be utilized in several ways depending on individual needs:

1. Photocopy directly onto acetate film for overhead projection during class lecture/discussion. The art is unlabeled so that the instructor may write directly on the acetate during class and emphasize critical features. A key advantage in the use of this form of visual presentation is the ease with which students are able to comprehend complex anatomical and physiological relationships presented during class.

2. Photocopy for handouts so that the students may take notes directly on the diagrams and in that way have a clear understanding of the relationship between the figure and lecture material.

3. If the course is on a tight budget, place masters of diagrams on reserve (usually in a notebook in the library) for students to make copies should they choose to do so.

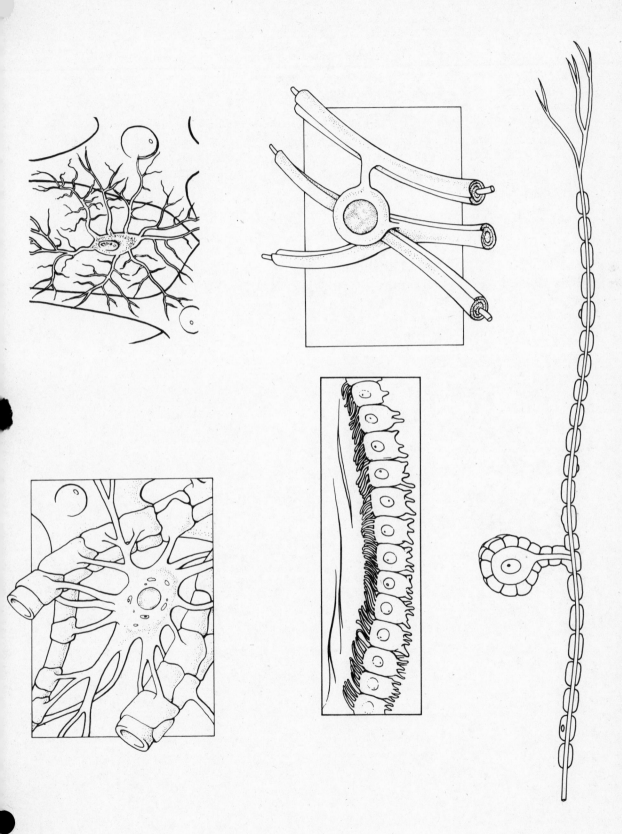

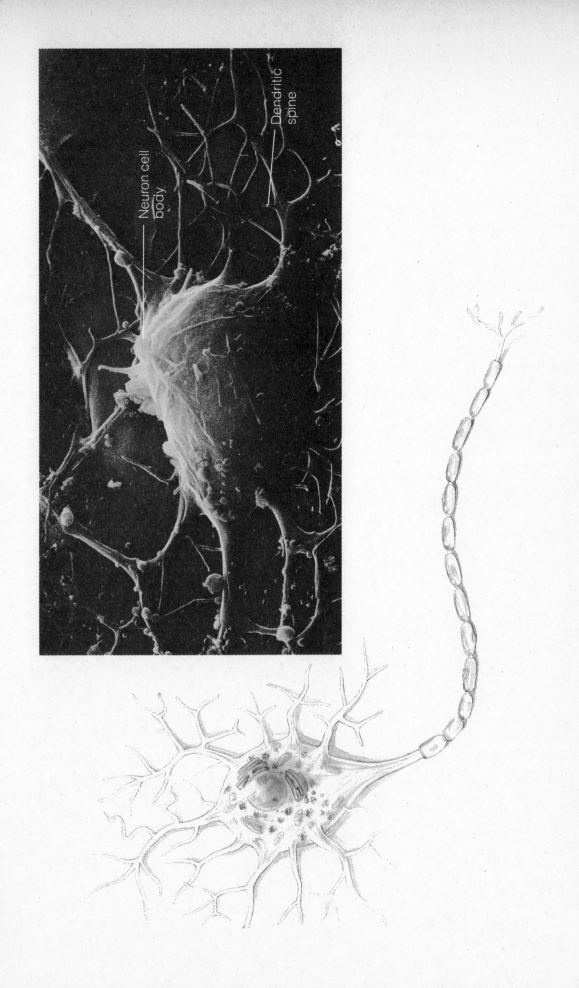

Neuron cell body

Dendritic spine

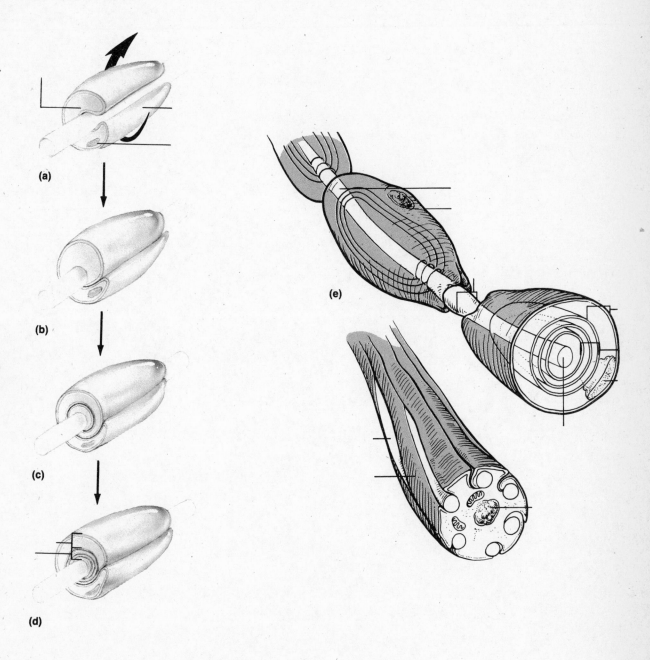

(a)

(b)

(c)

(d)

(e)

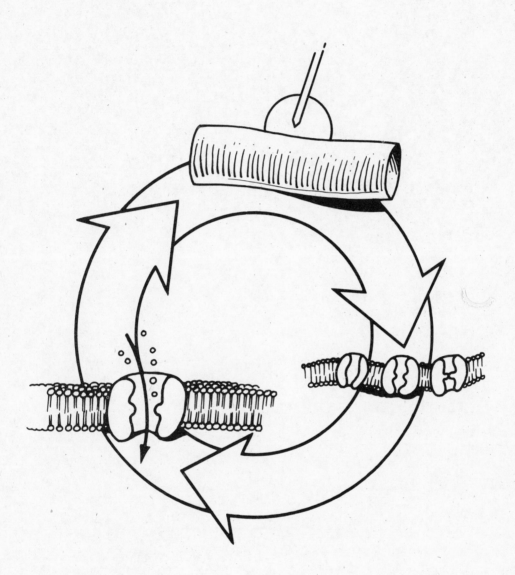

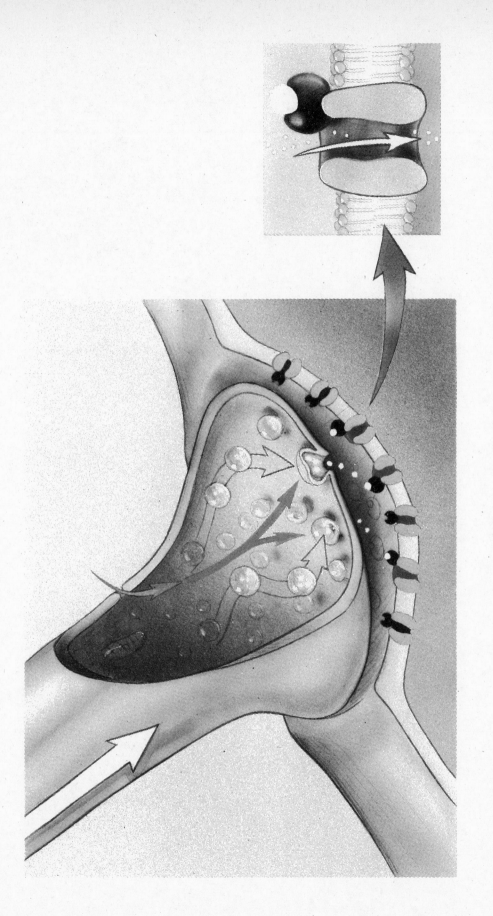

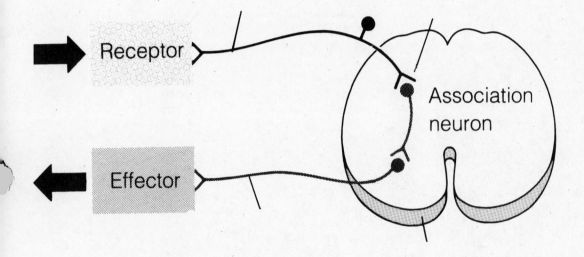

Receptor

Effector

Association
neuron

MATCHING QUESTIONS

Identify the following neuron parts by choosing the correct response from the key:

a. Axon   d. Dendrites
b. Axonal terminal   e. Nissl bodies
c. Cell body

____ 1. Neurotransmitters are released at the _____.
____ 2. The rough ER of the cell.
____ 3. Conducts impulses toward the nerve cell body.
____ 4. Conducts impulses away from the nerve cell body.

Qtype:»Memory   Outline:»III.B.   Text pp.»343-350
Answers:»1-b; 2-e; 3-d; 4-a

Match each term to the appropriate definition:

a. Action potential   d. Repolarization
b. Depolarization   e. Sodium-potassium pump
c. Absolute refractory period f. Relative refractory period

____ 1. Period during which the neuron cannot respond to a second stimulus, no matter how strong.
____ 2. The interior of the cell becomes less negative due to an influx of sodium ions.
____ 3. The specific period during which potassium ions diffuse out of the neuron due to a change in membrane permeability.
____ 4. Also called a nerve inpulse.
____ 5. An exceptionally strong stimulus can trigger a response.

Qtype:»Memory   Outline:»IV.C.   Text pp.»352-359
Answers:»1-c; 2-b; 3-d; 4-a; 5-f

Match the following:

a. Subthreshold stimulus   c. Temporal summation
b. Threshold stimulus   d. Spatial summation

____ 1. Numerous nerve impulses arriving at a synapse at closely timed intervals exert a cumulative effect.
____ 2. Stimulation of a postsynaptic neuron by many terminals at the same time.
____ 3. An insufficient stimulus.
____ 4. The intensity of stimulus below which no reponse is elicited in a neuron.

Qtype:»Memory   Outline:»IV.E.   Text pp.»362-365
Answers:»1-c; 2-d; 3-a; 4-b

TRUE/FALSE QUESTIONS

1. The All or None Law, as applied to nerve conduction states that the whole nerve cell must be stimulated for conduction to take place.

        a. true   b. false

Qtype:»Concept   Outline:»IV.C.3.d.   Text pp.»357
Answers:»false

---

2. Reflexes are rapid, automatic responses to stimuli.

        a. true   b. false

Qtype:»Memory   Outline:»V.C.1.b.   Text pp.»372
Answers:»true

---

3. A motor neuron carries stimuli from the central nervous system to the effector.

        a. true   b. false

Qtype:»Memory   Outline:»III.C.2.b.   Text pp.»349
Answers:»true

---

4. Efferent nerve fibers may be described as motor.

        a. true   b. false

Qtype:»Memory   Outline:»II.B.2.   Text pp.»342
Answers:»true

---

5. The velocity of conduction by nerve fibers can be modified by the length of the nerve fiber.

        a. true   b. false

Qtype:»Memory   Outline:»IV.C.3.g.   Text pp.»358
Answers:»false

---

6. Cell bodies of sensory neurons are located in ganglia lying outside the central nervous system.

        a. true   b. false

Qtype:»Memory   Outline:»III.B.3.   Text pp.»345
Answers:»true

---

7. Myelination of the nerve fibers in the central nervous system is the job of the oligodendrocyte.

        a. true   b. false

Qtype:»Memory   Outline:»III.A.2.d.   Text pp.»342
Answers:»true

---

8. During depolarization, the inside of the neuron's membrane becomes less negative.
    a. true   b. false

    Qtype:»Memory   Outline:»IV.C.1.a.   Text pp.»353
    Answers:»true

---

9. Neurons in the CNS are organized into functional groups.
    a. true   b. false

    Qtype:»Memory   Outline:»V.B.   Text pp.»371-372
    Answers:»true

---

10. Strong stimuli cause the amplitude of action potentials generated to increase.
    a. true   b. false

    Qtype:»Concept   Outline:»IV.C.3.d.   Text pp.»357
    Answers:»false

---

11. The oligodendrocytes are small branched cells of the CNS.
    a. true   b. false

    Qtype:»Memory   Outline:»III.A.2.   Text pp.»342
    Answers:»true

---

12. Neurons do **not** undergo mitosis in the adult.
    a. true   b. false

    Qtype:»Memory   Outline:»VI.A.   Text pp.»373-374
    Answers:»true

---

13. Enkephalins and endorphins are small peptides that mimic the action of heroin.
    a. true   b. false

    Qtype:»Memory   Outline:»IV.F.2.b.   Text pp.»368
    Answers:»true

---

14. Large nerve fibers conduct impulses more slowly than do small fibers.
    a. true   b. false

    Qtype:»Concept   Outline:»IV.C.3.g.   Text pp.»358
    Answers:»false

---

15. A synapse formed between the axonal ending of one neuron and the cell body of another neuron, is called an axosomatic synapse.

        a. true   b. false

Qtype:»Memory   Outline:»IV.D.1.   Text pp.»360
Answers:»true

16. In myelinated axons the voltage-gated sodium channels are concentrated at the nodes of Ranvier.

        a. true   b. false

Qtype:»Memory   Outline:»IV.C.3.g.   Text pp.»359
Answers:»true

17. Afferent neurons transmit impulses from the periphery to the CNS.

        a. true   b. false

Qtype:»Memory   Outline:»II.B.1.   Text pp.»342
Answers:»true

18. A stimulus traveling toward a synapse appears to open calcium gates at the presynaptic end, which in turn promote fusion of synaptic vesicles to the axonal membrane.

        a. true   b. false

Qtype:»Concept   Outline:»IV.D.3.b.   Text pp.»361
Answers:»true

19. Action potentials can be generated by virtually all cells of the body because all cells possess cell membranes.

        a. true   b. false

Qtype:»Concept   Outline:»IV.C.3.a.   Text pp.»354
Answers:»false

20. The Hodgkin cycle is the main force in the generation of graded potentials at receptor ends.

        a. true   b. false

Qtype:»Memory   Outline:»IV.C.E.b.   Text pp.»355
Answers:»false

21. If bacteria were to invade the CNS tissue, microglia would migrate to the area to engulf and destroy them.

        a. true   b. false

Qtype:»Concept   Outline:»III.A.2.b.   Text pp.»342
Answers:»true

22. Neurofibrils are also known as the rough ER, and play a role in protein synthesis.

    a. true   b. false

> Qtype:»Concept   Outline:»III.B.2.c.   Text pp.»344
> Answers:»false

23. The node of Ranvier is found only on myelinated neural processes.

    a. true   b. false

> Qtype:»Concept   Outline:»III.B.5.a   Text pp.»346
> Answers:»true

24. Voltage is always measured between two points and may be called the potential between these two points.

    a. true   b. false

> Qtype:»Concept   Outline:»IV.A.2.   Text pp.»350
> Answers:»true

25. Temporal summation occurs when the postsynaptic neuron is being stimulated by a large number of terminals from the same or different neurons at the same time.

    a. true   b. false

> Qtype:»Concept   Outline:»IV.E.3.a.   Text pp.»364
> Answers:»false

26. Neurons that are far away from the center of the neuron pool and are **not** easily excited by an incoming stimulus, are in the discharge zone.

    a. true   b. false

> Qtype:»Concept   Outline:»V.A.2.   Text pp.»371
> Answers:»false

MULTIPLE-CHOICE QUESTIONS

1. Ionotropic neurotransmitters:
   a. require cyclic AMP.
   b. activate the Hodgkin cycle.
   c. mediate very slow responses.
   d. open ion channels directly.
   e. All of the above are correct.

> Qtype:»Concept   Outline:»IV.F.3.b.   Text pp.»368
> Answers:»d

2. Which of the following is correct relative to Ohm's law?
   a. I=R/V
   b. Current is directly proportional to the voltage.
   c. R=V+I
   d. The more intense the stimulus the more voltage changes.
   e. All of the above are true.

Qtype:»Concept   Outline:»IV.A.5.   Text pp.»350
Answers:»b

3. Graded potentials exhibit all the following except they:
   a. are short lived.
   b. can form on receptor endings.
   c. increase amplitude as they move away from the stimulus point.
   d. can be called postsynaptic potentials.

Qtype:»Concept   Outline:»IV.C.2.   Text pp.»353-354
Answers:»c

4. The nervous system exhibits all the major functions except:
   a. monitors changes.   c. stores calcium.
   b. integrates impulses.   d. effects responses.

Qtype:»Concept   Outline:»I.B.   Text pp.»340-341
Answers:»c

5. Ciliated CNS neuroglia that play an active role in forming and moving the cerebrospinal fluid would be:
   a. ependyma cells.   c. oligodendrocytes.
   b. Schwann cells.   d. astrocytes.

Qtype:»Memory   Outline:»III.A.2.c.   Text pp.»342
Answers:»a

6. The Sheath of Schwann is also called:
   a. myelin sheath.   c. neurilemma.
   b. axolemma.   d. white matter.

Qtype:»Memory   Outline:»III.B.5.8.   Text pp.»346
Answers:»c

7. Bipolar cells are commonly:
   a. motor neurons.
   b. called neuroglia.
   c. found in ganglia.
   d. found in the retina of the eye.

   Qtype:»Memory   Outline:»III.C.1.b.   Text pp.»346
   Answers:»d

8. An excitatory neurotransmitter secreted by motor neurons innervating skeletal muscle is:
   a. cholinesterase.   d. acetylcholine.
   b. norepinephrine.   e. gamma aminobutyric acid.
   c. ATP.

   Qtype:»Memory   Outline:»IV.F.2.   Text pp.»366
   Answers:»d

9. A neural circuit that would cause a single impulse to be transmitted over and over would
   be a:
   a. parallel circuit.   d. reverberating circuit.
   b. diverging circuit.   e. repetitive circuit.
   c. converging circuit.

   Qtype:»Memory   Outline:»V.B.3.   Text pp.»372
   Answers:»d

10. The period after an initial stimulus when a neuron is **not** sensitive to another stimulus is
    the:
    a. resting period.   d. transient period.
    b. repolarization.   e. refractory period.
    c. depolarization.

    Qtype:»Memory   Outline:»IV.C.3.f.   Text pp.»358
    Answers:»e

11. In terms of neuronal circuits, one type which is involved in concentrating or directing a
    large number of incoming impulses to a rather small number of neurons, is called a:
    a. diverging circuit.   c. converging circuit.
    b. oscillating circuit.   d. parallel circuit.

    Qtype:»Memory   Outline:»V.B.2.   Text pp.»372
    Answers:»c

12. A second nerve impulse cannot be generated until:
    a. the membrane potential has been reestablished.
    b. the Na ions have been pumped back into the cell.
    c. proteins have been resynthesized.
    d. All of the above are correct.

    Qtype:»Concept   Outline:»IV.C.3.f.   Text pp.»358
    Answers:»a

13. Which of the following is **not** a structural feature of a neuron?
    a. synaptic cleft   c. dendrites
    b. nissl bodies   d. axon

    Qtype:»Memory   Outline:»III.B.1.   Text pp.»343-350
    Answers:»a

14. The part of a neuron that conducts impulses away from its cell body is called:
    a. an axon.   c. a neurolemma.
    b. a dendrite.   d. a Schwann cell.

    Qtype:»Memory   Outline:»III.B.5.d.   Text pp.»345
    Answers:»a

15. If one incoming impulse causes several outgoing nerve impulses, we know that there is a(n):
    a. converging circuit.   d. reverberating circuit.
    b. concentration effect.   e. parallel circuit.
    c. diverging circuit.

    Qtype:»Concept   Outline:»V.B.1.   Text pp.»371-372
    Answers:»c

16. The point at which an impulse from one nerve cell is communicated to another nerve cell is the:
    a. cell body.   c. receptor.
    b. synapse.   d. effector.

    Qtype:»Memory   Outline:»IV.D.1.   Text pp.»360
    Answers:»b

17. The role of cholinesterase is to:
    a. act as a transmitting agent.
    b. to amplify or enhance the effect of ACH.
    c. to destroy ACH a brief period after its release by the axonal endings.
    d. cause tension.

    Qtype:»Memory   Outline:»IV.F.2.a.   Text pp.»367
    Answers:»c

18. Which of the following is **not** a function of the autonomic nervous system?
    a. innervation of visceral organs
    b. regulation and control of vital activities
    c. innervation of glands
    d. conscious control of motor activities

    Qtype:»Concept   Outline:»II.B.2.b.   Text pp.»342
    Answers:»d

19. Collections of nerve cell bodies outside the central nervous system are called:
    a. nuclei.   c. ganglia.
    b. nerves.   d. tracts.

    Qtype:»Memory   Outline:»III.B.3.   Text pp.»345
    Answers:»c

20. The term "central nervous system" refers to the:
    a. autonomic nervous system.
    b. brain, spinal cord, and peripheral nerves.
    c. brain and spinal cord.
    d. spinal cord and spinal nerves.

    Qtype:»Memory   Outline:»II.A.   Text pp.»341
    Answers:»c

21. The substance released at axonal endings to propagate a nervous inpulse is called a(n):
    a. ion.
    b. cholinesterase.
    c. neurotransmitter.
    d. None of the above are correct.

    Qtype:»Memory   Outline:»IV.F.1.   Text pp.»365
    Answers:»b

22. A neuron which has its primary function the job or action of connecting other neurons is called:
    a. a motor neuron.   c. an association neuron.
    b. a sensory neuron.   d. a glial cell.

    Qtype:»Memory   Outline:»III.C.2.c.   Text pp.»350
    Answers:»c

23. Saltatory conduction is a result of:
    a. myelin sheath.
    b. large nerve fibers.
    c. diphasic impulses.
    d. erratic transmission of nerve impulses.

    Qtype:»Concept   Outline:»IV.C.3.g.   Text pp.»359
    Answers:»a

24. Which of these ions is actively transported through the cell membrane to establish a resting potential?
    a. Na   d. Mg
    b. Cl   e. Ca
    c. HCO3

    Qtype:»Memory   Outline:»IV.B.1.   Text pp.»352
    Answers:»a

25. In what way does the interior of a resting (non-conducting) neuron differ from the external environment? The interior is:
    a. positively charged and contains less sodium
    b. negatively charged and contains less sodium
    c. negatively charged and contains more sodium
    d. positively charged and contains more sodium

    Qtype:»Concept   Outline:»IV.B.1.   Text pp.»352
    Answers:»b

26. The part of the neuron that acts as receptor region is called:
    a. an axon.   c. a neurolemma.
    b. a dendrite.   d. a Schwann cell.

    Qtype:»Memory   Outline:»III.B..5.d.   Text pp.»345
    Answers:»b

27. Which of the following is true about the movement of ions across excitable living membranes?
    a. Ions can always move passively across membranes to some degree.
    b. Some ions move down their concentration gradients through chemically sensitive membrane proteins.
    c. Ion gates in the membrane can open in response to electrical potential changes.
    d. Only b and c are correct.
    e. a, b, and c are correct.

    Qtype:»Concept   Outline:»IV.A.6.   Text pp.»350
    Answers:»e

28. Choose the statement that is most correct about membrane potential:
    a. Voltage is measured by placing two electrodes on the exterior surface of the membrane.
    b. The ions involved in maintaining the resting state of a neuron always leak up their concentration gradients.
    c. The solutions that make up the cytoplasm and interstitial fluids are electrically neutral.
    d. The interior of the cell is positively charged with respect to the environment.
    e. None of the above are correct.

> Qtype:»Concept   Outline:»IV.B.   Text pp.»351-352
> Answers:»c

29. If a neuron were experimentally placed in conditions where intracellular potassium were depleted, which of the following is a logical consequence?
    1. The neuron would hyperpolarize.
    2. There would be a reduction in membrane potential.
    3. The neuron would spontaneously "fire".
    a. 1 only   d. 1 and 3
    b. 2 only   e. 2 and 3
    c. 3 only

> Qtype:»Concept   Outline:»IV.C.   Text pp.»353
> Answers:»a

30. The electrical activity of a neuron:
    a. involves a positive feedback mechanism in impulse propagation.
    b. involves the influx of negative ions to depolarize the membrane.
    c. is initiated by potassium ion movement.
    d. involves impulse propagation dependent on chemically gated ion channels.
    e. All the above are correct.

> Qtype:»Concept   Outline:»IV.C.3.   Text pp.»354-355
> Answers:»a

31. If a motor neuron in the body were stimulated by an electrode placed about midpoint along the length of the axon:
    1. the impulse would move to axon terminal only.
    2. muscle contraction would occur.
    3. the impulse would spread bidirectionally.
    a. 1 only   d. 1 and 3
    b. 2 only   e. 2 and 3
    c. 3 only

> Qtype:»Concept   Outline:»IV.C.3.c.   Text pp.»356
> Answers:»e

32. Neurons may be classified according to several characteristics. Which of the following is correct?
    a. Group A fibers are mostly somatic sensory and motor and ar the smallest in diameter.
    b. Group B fibers are highly myelinated and have the highest conduction velocities.
    c. Group C fibers are not capable of saltatory conduction.
    d. Small cross-sectional area allows shorter conduction times.
    e. Myelinated axons conduct impulses slowly due to the "insulation" inhibiting ion flow in some areas of the membrane.

    Qtype:»Concept   Outline:»IV.C.3.g.   Text pp.»359
    Answers:»c

33. Select the correct statement about synapses:
    a. Cells with interconnected cytoplasm are chemically coupled.
    b. The release of neurotransmitter molecules gives cells the property of being electrically coupled.
    c. Neurotransmitter receptors are located on the axons of cells.
    d. The synaptic cleft prevents an impulse from being transmitted directly from one neuron to another.
    e. Many synaptic vesicles collect in the dendrites of nerve fibers.

    Qtype:»Concept   Outline:»IV.D.   Text pp.»360-362
    Answers:»d

34. Excitatory and inhibitory potentials differ from action potentials in several ways. Which of the following is not correct?
    a. Excitatory synapses are chemically gated.
    b. Sodium and potassium movement is sequential.
    c. Even if enough neurotransmitter is bound, an EPSP can not stimulate an action potential.
    d. IPSPs involve hyperpolarization.
    e. Chloride influx or potassium efflux can dause an IPSP.

    Qtype:»Concept   Outline:»IV.E.   Text pp.»362-365
    Answers:»b

35. Neuromodulators:
        1. can influence the uptake of neurotransmitters.
        2. influence the sensitivity of the postsynaptic neuron.
        3. can act as hormones.
    a. 1 only   d. 1 and 3
    b. 2 only   e. 1, 2, and 3
    c. 3 only

    Qtype:»Concept   Outline:»IV.E.3.c.   Text pp.»365
    Answers:»e

36. Place the following parts of the reflex arc in proper sequence:
    a. effector-motor neuron-integration center-sensory neuron-receptor
    b. receptor-motor neuron-integration center-sensory neuron-effector
    c. receptor-sensory neuron-integration center-motor neuron-effector
    d. effector-sensory neuron-integration center-motor neuron-receptor
    e. sensory neuron-receptor-integration center-effector-motor neuron

    Qtype:»Memory   Outline:»V.C.1.b.   Text pp.»372
    Answers:»c

37. Select the statement(s) that (is/are) correct about the functional components of neurons:
    1. The conducting component usually transmits impulses away from the cell body
    2. The secretory component causes the release of chemical substances.
    3. Axon terminals are the conducting component.
    a. 1 only   d. 1 and 2
    b. 2 only   e. 2 and 3
    c. 3 only

    Qtype:»Concept   Outline:»III.B.5.   Text pp.»345
    Answers:»d

38. Select the correct statement about the mechanism of termination of the neurotransmitter effect:
    1. Enzymatic degredation of neurotransmitter on the postsynaptic membrane.
    2. Reuptake of neurotransmitter by the postsynaptic membrane.
    3. Simple diffusion of neurotransmitter away from the synapse.
    a. 1 only   d. 1 and 3
    b. 2 only   e. 2 and 3
    c. 3 only

    Qtype:»Concept   Outline:»IV.D.3.   Text pp.»362
    Answers:»d

39. In synaptic potentiation:
    a. presynaptic cells at such synapses contain more sodium than usual.
    b. calcium gates are involved.
    c. slight inhibition of the postsynaptic cell results.
    d. smaller postsynaptic potentials are produced than would normally be expected.
    e. Both d and d are correct.

    Qtype:»Concept   Outline:»IV.E.3.b.   Text pp.»365
    Answers:»b

SHORT-ANSWER QUESTIONS

1. Imagine the following possible condition: a neuron which has several hundred axonal knobs impinging on it. The majority of these axonal knobs are shown to be "firing." However, the neuron in question does not transmit an impulse. Give a valid explanation of why this could occur.

> Qtype:»Concept   Outline:»IV.E.   Text pp.»362-365
> Answers:»Both excitatory and inhibitory potentials impinge on neurons. Inhibitory (IPSP)
> are "firing", but due to the neurotransmitter released and its action, the postsynaptic
> neuron is inhibited from "firing" (hyperpolarized).

2. Define neurotransmitter. Name two amino acid neurotransmitters, two catecholamines and two peptides.

> Qtype:»Concept   Outline:»IV.F.   Text pp.»365-370
> Answers:»Neurotransmitters are chemical signals used as means of communication.
> GABA and glycine are amino acid neurotransmitters, dopamine and morepinephrine are
> catecholamines, and endorphin and enkephalin are peptide transmitters.

CLINICAL QUESTIONS

1. Mr. Kelly staggered home after a "rough night" at the local pub. While attempting to navigate the stairs, he passed out cold and laid (all night) with his right armpit straddling the staircase bannister. When he awoke the next morning, he had a severe headache, but what bothered him more was that he had no sensation in his right arm and hand which also appeared to be paralyzed. Explain.

> Qtype:»Application Outline:»IV.C.3.g.   Text pp.»359
> Answers:»Continuous pressure interrupts blood flow along with oxygen and nutrients to
> the neuronal processes. As a result, impulse transmission is inhibited temporarily.

The Central Nervous System

12

CHAPTER PREVIEW

This chapter focuses on the structures of the central nervous system and touches on the functions associated with its specific anatomical regions. The human brain and all its divisions, the meninges, and the cerebrospinal fluid circulation, along with the spinal cord and all its tracts, will be described in detail.

AT A GLANCE

INTEGRATING THE PACKAGE

SUGGESTED LECTURE OUTLINE

I. Introduction (p. 378)

II. The Brain (pp. 379-407)
    A. Embryonic Development of the Brain (pp. 379-380)
        1. Ectodermal Derivations (Fig. 12.2, p. 379)
            a. Neural Plate

    b. Neural Folds
    c. Neural Tube
    d. Neural Crest
  2. Primary Brain Vesicles
      a. Prosencephalon (Forebrain)
      b. Mesencephalon (Midbrain)
      c. Rhombencephalon (Hindbrain)
  3. Secondary Brain Vesicles
      a. Telencephalon
      b. Diencephalon
      c. Metencephalon
      d. Myelencephalon
      e. Mesencephalon
B. Regions of the Brain (p. 381, Fig. 12.5, p. 379)
C. Ventricles of the Brain (pp. 381-382; Fig. 12.6, p. 380)
    1. Lateral Ventricles
    2. Third Ventricle
    3. Fourth Ventricle
D. The Cerebral Hemispheres (pp. 382-392)
    1. Surface Anatomy
        a. Gyri
        b. Sulci
        c. Fissures
            1. Longitudinal Fissure
            2. Transverse Fissure
        d. Lobes
            1. Frontal
            2. Parietal
            3. Occipital
            4. Temporal
            5. Insula (Island of Reil)
    2. Cerebral Cortex
        a. Localization of Cortical Functions
        b. Generalization of Cortical Functions
        c. Motor Areas (Fig. 12.10, p. 387)
            1. Primary (Somatic) Motor Cortex
            2. Premotor Cortex
            3. Broca's Area
        d. Sensory Areas (Fig. 12.10, p. 387)
            1. Primary Sensory Cortex
            2. Somatosensory Association Cortex
            3. Visual Cortex
            4. Auditory Area
            5. Olfactory Area
            6. Gustatory Area
        e. Association Areas
            1. Prefrontal Cortex
            2. General Interporetation Area
            3. Affective Language Areas
        f. Lateralization of Cortical Functioning
    3. Cerebral White Matter (Fig. 12.11, p. 390)
        a. Commissural Fibers
        b. Association Fibers
        c. Projection Fibers

2. The Reticular Formation (Fig. 12.19, p. 402)
    a. Location
    b. Reticular Activating System
    c. General Functions
I. Protection of the Brain (pp. 402-403
    1. Cranium
    2. Meninges (Fig. 12.20, p. 403)
        a. Dura Mater
        b. Arachnoid
        c. Pia Mater
    3. Cerebrospinal Fluid
        a. General Characteristics
        b. Choroid Plexus
        c. Circulation
    4. Blood-Brain Barrier
J. Homeostatic Imbalances of the Brain (pp. 405-406)
    1. Traumatic Brain Injuries
        a. Concussion
        b. Contusion
        c. Cerebral Edema
    2. Degenerative Brain Diseases
        a. Cerebrovascular Accidents
        b. Alzheimer's Disease
        c. Multiple Sclerosis

III. The Spinal Cord (pp. 407-416)

A. Gross Anatomy and Protection of the Spinal Cord (pp. 407-408)
    1. Basic Characteristics
    2. Meningeal Coverings
    3. Conus Medullaris
    4. Filum Terminale
    5. Spinal Cord Enlargements
    6. Cauda Equina
B. Embryonic Development of the Spinal Cord (p. 408)
C. Cross-Sectional Anatomy of the Spinal Cord (pp. 409-414)
    1. Gray Matter and Spinal Roots
        a. Gray Commissure
        b. Lateral Gray Masses
            1. Posterior Horns
            2. Anterior Horns
            3. Lateral Horns
        c. Roots
            1. Ventral Roots
            2. Dorsal Roots
        d. Dorsal Root Ganglia
        e. Spinal Nerves
    2. White Matter of the Spinal Cord
        a. Funiculi
            1. Posterior
            2. Lateral
            3. Anterior
        b. Functional Generalizations
        c. Ascending Pathways and Tracts
            1. General Characteristics

CROSS-REFERENCES

---

1. The role of the medulla in cardiac rate regulation is described in Chapter 19, p. 619.

2. Testosterone and development of the brain is further explained in Chapter 28, pp. 945-946.

3. The role of the hypothalamus in regulation of fluid and electrolyte balance is detailed in Chapter 27.

4. The role of the hypothalamus in body temperature regulation is presented in Chapter 25, p. 864.

5. Central nervous involvement in the reflex activity controlling digestive processes is mentioned in Chapter 24, p. 788

6. The respiratory centers in the medulla and pons are covered in Chapter 23, pp. 754-755.

7. Cortical and hypothalamic involvement in respiration is explained in Chapter 23, pp. 756-757.

8. The capillaries of the brain (blood-brain barrier) are further explained in Chapter 20, p. 651.

9. The medulla and regulation of blood vessel diameter (vasomotor center) is examined in Chapter 20, p. 642.

10. The hypothalamus and blood pressure regulation is mentioned in Chapter 20, p. 644.

11. The hypothalamus and hormone production is examined in great detail in Chapter 17, p. 547, 551-552.

12. The role of the cerebral cortex and cerebellum in sensory information integration is further examined in Chapter 16.

13. The role of the thalamus in the special senses is mentioned in Chapter 16.

14. The different brain areas and neural integration are examined in Chapter 15, p. 479-485.

15. Spinal roots and peripheral nervous system function is presented in Chapters 13, p. 428; 14, p. 460.

16. The relationship between the peripheral nervous system and gray and white matter of the spinal cord are explained in Chapters 13, pp. 424-430; and 14, p. 460-466.

ANSWERS TO TEXTBOOK CHAPTER QUESTIONS

Multiple Choice/Matching

1. a

2. (1)c; (2)f; (3)e; (4)g; (5)b; (6)f; (7)i; (8)a

3. d

4. c

5. a

6. b

7. c

8. a

9. (1)a; (2)b; (3)a; (4)a; (5)b; (6)a; (7)b; (8)b; (9)a

10. d

Short Answer Essay Questions

11. See Fig. 12.3, p. 380, for a diagram of the embryonic brain vesicles.

12. a. Increases cortical surface area. (p. 383)

b. Sulci and fissures (p. 379); gyri (p. 382)
c. Median longitudinal fissure (p. 382)
d. Central sulcus; lateral sulcus (p. 382)

13. a. See Fig. 12.9, p. 386, for a drawing of the functional areas of the brain.
   b. Primary motor cortex - All voluntary somatic motor responses arise from this region.
   Premotor cortex - This region controls learned motor skills of a repetitious or patterned nature.
   Somatosensory association area - Acts to integrate and analyze different somatosensory inputs, such as temperature, touch, pressure, and pain.
   Primary sensory area - Receives all somatosensory information from receptors located in the skin and from proprioceptors in muscles; identifies the body region being stimulated.
   Visual area - Receives information that originates in the retinas of the eyes.
   Auditory area - Receives information that originates in the hearing receptors of the inner ear.
   Prefrontal cortex - Most involved with elaboration of thought, intelligence, motivation, and personality. It also associates experiences necessary for the production of abstract ideas, judgment, planning, and conscience, and is important in planning motor activity.
   Wernicke's area - Speech area involved in the comprehension of language, especially when the word needs to be sounded out or related.
   Broca's area - Previously called the motor speech area; now known to be active in many other activities as well.

14. a. Specialization of cortical functions. The "dominant" hemisphere excells at language and mathematical skills. The nondominant hemisphere is better at visual-spatial skills, intuition, emotion, and appreciation of art and music. (pp. 389-390)
   b. Both hemispheres have perfect and instant communication with each other so there is tremendous integration, therefore neither side is better at everything. However, each hemisphere does have unique abilities not shared by its partner. (p. 389)

15. a. Initiate slow and sustained movement; helps to coordinate and control motor activity (p. 392)
   b. The putamen and globus pallidus (p. 392)
   c. Caudate nucleus (p. 392)

16. a. Three paired fiber tracts (cerebellar peduncles) connect it to the brain stem. (pp. 399-400)
   b. The cerebellum has a convoluted surface with gray matter on outside and white on inside; it has two hemispheres that have overlapping functions. (pp. 399-400)

17. The cerebellum acts like an automatic pilot by initiating and coordinating the activity of skeletal muscle groups. A step-by-step discussion is given on p. 398.

18. a. Medial aspect of each cerebral hemisphere.
   b. Cingulate gyrus, parahippocampal gyrus, hippocampus, regions of the hypothalamus, mammillary bodies, septal nuclei, amygdaloid nucleus, anterior thalamic nuclei, and fornix.
   c. Acts as our emotional or affective (feeling) brain. (p. 400)

19. a. It extends through the central core of the medulla, pons, and midbrain.
   b. RAS means reticular activating system, which is our cortical arousal mechanism. It helps to keep the cerebral cortex alert while filtering out unimportant inputs.(pp. 401-402)

20. CNS protected by: bony cranium, meninges, cerebrospinal fluid and blood brain barrier. (pp. 402-405)

21. a. CSF is formed by the choroid plexus via a secretiry process involving both active transport and diffusion and is drained by the arachnoid villi. See Fig. 12.20 for the circulatory pathway. (p. 404)
   b. A condition called hydrocephalus can develop. In children, the fontanels allow expansion without brain damage, but in adults, the lack of expansion may cause severe damage due to brain compression. (p. 405)

22. The blood-brain barrier represents capillaries that are formed by endothelial cells joined by tight junctions. This characteristic makes them highly selective, insuring that only certain substances can gain access to the neural tissue. (p. 405)

23. a. A concussion occurs when brain injury is slight and the symptoms are mild and transient. Contusions occur when marked tissue destruction takes place. (p. 406)
    b. Due to injury of the RAS. (p. 402)

24. The spinal cord is somewhat flattened from front to back and is marked by two grooves: the anterior median fissure and the posterior median sulcus. The gray matter of the spinal cord is shaped like the letter "H" consisting of lateral gray masses connected by the gray commissure. The two posterior (dorsal) projections are the posterior horns and the anterior (ventral) projections are the anterior horns. Somatic motor neurons send their axons out via the ventral roots, and sensory axons enter the cord via the dorsal roots. The white matter of the cord is composed of myelinated and unmyelinated fibers that run in three possible directions: (1) up to higher CNS centers, (2) Down to the cord from the brain, and (3) across from one side of the cord to another. The white matter on each side of the cord is divided into three white columns, posterior, lateral, and anterior funiculi. (pp. 407-416)

25. Touch and pressure: fasciculus cuneatus, fasciculus gracilis, and anterior spinothalamic. Proprioception: anterior and posterior spinocerebellar. Pain and temperature: lateral spinothalamic (Table 12.2, p. 412)

26. a. Voluntary skeletal movements (pyramidal tracts) - lateral and anterior corticospinal.
    b. Tectospinal, vestibulospinal, rubrospinal. (Table 12.3, p. 416)

27. Spastic paralysis - due to damage to upper motor neurons of the primary motor cortex. Muscles can respond to reflex arcs. (p. 414)
    Flaccid paralysis - damage to ventral root or anterior horn cells. Muscles cannot respond.

28. Paraplegia - damage to cord (lower motor neurons) between T1 and L1 that causes paralysis of both lower limbs.
    Hemiplegia - damage, usually in the brain, that causes paralysis of one side of the body.
    Quadriplegia - damage to cord in cervical area affecting all four limbs. (p. 416)

29. a. CVA, also known as stroke, occurs when blood circulation to a brain area is blocked and vital brain tissue dies. New hypothesis targets the release of glutamate by oxygen starved neurons (and subsequent entry of excess Ca^{++}) as the culprit. (p. 406)
    b. Any event that kills brain tissue due to a lack of oxygen; includes blockage of a cerebral artery by a blood clot, compression of brain tissue by hemorrhage or edema, and arteriosclerosis. Consequences include paralysis, sensory deficits, language difficulties, and speech problems. (p. 406)

30. a. Continued myelination of neural tissue account for growth and maturation of the nervous system.
    b. There is a decline in brain weight and volume in aging. (p. 419)

Critical Thinking and Application Questions

1. a. Only likely diagnosis is hydrocephalus.
   b. CT or sonograms, but most importantly pneumoencephalography.
   c. Later and third ventricles enlarge, fourth ventricle, central canal and subarachnois space are not affected. If arachnoid villi are obstructed, all CSF areas will be enlarged. (p. 405)

2. Alzheimer's disease (pp. 406-407)

3. Probably the frontal lobes, specifically the prefrontal cortex which mediated personality and moral behavior. (p. 388)

LABORATORY CORRELATIONS

1. Marieb, E. N. <u>Human Anatomy and Physiology Laboratory Manual: Cat and Fetal Pig Versions</u>. 3rd. ed. Benjamin/Cummings, 1989.

   Exercise 18: Gross Anatomy of the Brain and Cranial Nerves
   Exercise 19: Spinal Cord, Spinal Nerves, and Autonomic Nervous System
   Exercise 23: Electroencephalography

2. Marieb, E. N. <u>Human Anatomy and Physiology Laboratory Manual: Brief Version</u>. 3rd. ed. Benjamin/Cummings, 1992.

   Exercise 16: Gross Anatomy of the Brain and Cranial Nerves
   Exercise 17: Electroencephalography
   Exercise 18: Spinal Cord, Spinal Nerves, and Autonomic Nervous system

OVERHEAD TRANSPARENCIES INDEX

Transparency	Description
12.3	Embryonic development of the human brain
12.5a	Regions of the brain
12.6	3-D views of the ventricles of the brain
12.7a/b	Lobes and fissures of the cerebral hemispheres. (a) left lateral view. (b) Medial surface of the right hemisphere
12.7c	(c) Superior view
12.8	Major regions of the cerebral hemispheres
12.9	Functional areas of the left cerebral cortex
12.10	Sensory and motor areas of cerebral cortex
12.12	Basal nuclei
12.13a	Diencephalon and brain stem structures
12.20a	Meninges of the brain
12.20b	Location and circulatory pattern of cerebrospinal fluid
12.21a	Structure of the spinal cord

12.23b	3-d view of adult spinal cord w/ meningeal cov.
12.25	Pathways of ascending spinal cord tracts
12.26	Pathways of descending spinal cord tracts

BASSETT ATLAS SLIDES AND FIGURES INDEX

Slide #	Figure	Description
1	1.1	Brain surface and vessels
2	1.2	Meninges and vessels
3	1.3	Brain surface with and without vessels
4	1.4A,B	Cross-section of the brain
5	1.5A,B	Base of the brain
6	1.6	Circle of Willis
7	1.7	Posterior view of the brain in situ
8	1.8A,B	Sagittal section of the brain
9	1.9A,B	Spinal cord, origin
10	1.10	Spinal cord, cauda equina
11	1.11A,B	Spinal cord, detail

BLACK LINE MASTER INDEX

Black Line Master	Description
12.5a	Regions of the brain
12.6	3-d views of the ventricles of the brain
12.7a/b/c	Lobes and fissures of the cerebral hemispheres
12.8	Major regions of the cerebral hemispheres
12.9	Functional areas of the left cerebral cortex

INSTRUCTIONAL AIDS

LECTURE HINTS

1. Study of the central nervous system is difficult for most students. The complexity of the material can overwhelm the best of individuals. Initially present the material from an overall conceptual perspective, then progress into greater levels of detail. In this way, students are not as likely to get "lost".

2. When discussing the ventricles, do a rough diagram on the board (or acetate) that shows a schematic representation of the chambers and connecting passageways. As students comprehend the serial nature of CSF flow, translate the sketches to actual cross-sectional photographs or accurate diagrams.

3. Students often have difficulty understanding how the cerebellum is involved in the control of motor activity. Try using a physical activity such as golf to illustrate cerebellar interaction, i.e., we all know how to swing a club but only well developed cerebellar coordination of muscle group action allows a "pro" to place the ball exactly where it should be.

4. Emphasize that the meningeal protection of the brain and spinal cord are continuous, but that the spinal cord has an epidural space whereas the brain does not.

DEMONSTRATIONS/ACTIVITIES

1. Film(s) or other audiovisual materials of choice.

2. Obtain a 3-D model of a human brain and compare it to a real human brain and/or a dissected sheep brain.

3. Obtain a 3-D model of a spinal cord, both longitudinal section and cross section to illustrate its features.

4. Obtain stained sections of brain tissue to illustrate the differences between gray and white matter and to show internal parts.

5. Obtain a 3-D model or cast of the ventricles of the brain.

6. Obtain a sheep brain with the cranium and/or meninges still intact.

7. Project or set up microslides to demonstrate cross-sectional anatomy of the spinal cord at several different levels to show how gray and white matter changes with level in the cord.

CRITICAL THINKING/DISCUSSION TOPICS

1. Discuss the difference between encephalitis and meningitis.

2. Prefrontal lobotomies have been used in psychotherapy along with electrical shock. How and why have these techniques been used?

3. Since a right-handed person's left hemisphere appears to dominate in cerebral functions, what could be done to increase the use of the left hemisphere?

4. Anencephalic children will always die soon after birth. There is currently a desire among some medical groups to use the organs of these children to help others. What are the pros and cons of this type of organ transplantation?

5. If a needle is used to deliver or remove fluids from the spaces surrounding the spinal cord, where is the best location (along the length of the cord) to perform the procedure? Why?

6. Trace the complete path of CSF from formation to reabsorption and examine the consequences if choroid plexus function were altered, or an obstruction developed in the path of CSF flow.

LIBRARY RESEARCH TOPICS

1. What techniques are currently used to localize and treat tumors of the brain?

2. How has the human brain changed in size and shape over the millions of years of evolution? Explore the development of the human nervous system.

3. What drugs are being used to enhance memory? Where and how do they work?

4. The sensory and motor areas of the cerebral cortex around the pre- and post-central gyrus have been carefully mapped out. How was this done?

5. What methods of experimentation have been used to study the limbic system? What research has been done on determining whether some habitual criminals have defects in this system?

6. Describe the latest techniques used to examine structure/function of the CNS.

7. How can fetal tissues be used to repair adult CNS dysfunctions?

Films

1. Spinal Cord and Its Relations (TF, 13 min., C.) Dissection of a spinal cord on an injected cadaver. Also available on video.

2. Cerebrospinal Fluid (IOWA, 3 min., C, 1971, silent) Illustrates the composition and function of cerebrospinal fluid and factors that influence its pressure within the central nervous system.

3. Exploring the Human Brain (BFA, 18 min., C, 1977) Historical development of the understanding of the human brain from the time of Hippocrates.

4. The Hidden Universe: The Brain, Part 1; Part 2 (MGHT, 48 min., C, 1977) Covers functions of the brain and illustrates a craniotomy.

5. The Human Brain - A Dynamic View of its Structures and its Organization (RL, 29 min., C, 1976) Computer visualization of the brain as a three-dimensional structure.

Filmstrips/Slides

1. The Central Nervous System (NTA, #69, Microviewer)

2. Spinal Cord, Nerves, and Reflexes (PHM)

3. Exploring the Brain: The Newest Frontier, Parts 1-5 (HRM)

4. Introductory Physiology Series: The Nervous System (MGHT)

5. Nervous System and Its Function (EI)

6. Nervous Systems(EI)

Videotapes

1. The Addicted Brain (FHS, QB-1363, 26 min., C, VHS/BETA) Documentary explores drug use and effect on brain.

2. The Sexual Brain (FHS, QB-1416, 28 min., C, VHS/BETA) Study of the brain illustrating the differences between males and females.

3. Our Talented Brain (FHS, QB-833, 26 min., C, VHS/BETA) Program explores neural structure and physiology of the brain. Also available in 16mm.

4. The Anatomical Basis of the Brain Function Series (TF, C, 1988) Twenty titles, ranging from 14 to 23 minutes, presenting virtually every aspect of human brain neuroanatomy.

5. The Neuroanatomy Series (TF, C, 1988) Twenty-four titles, ranging from 15 to 51 minutes, presenting the dissection of the human brain.

6. Brain Triggers (PLP, CH-770234, VHS).

7. Your Body, Part 3 (PLP, CH-140203, VHS).

Computer Software

1. The Human Brain: Neurons (PLP, R-51003, Apple) Explores neuron structures, types of neurons, potentials, and neurotransmitters.

2. Body Language, Study of Human Anatomy, Nervous System (PLP, CH-182013, Apple; CH-182014, IBM).

3. The Human Brain: Neurons (PLP, CH-510003, Apple).

See *Guide to Audiovisual Resources* at the end of this module for key to AV distributors

---

LECTURE ENHANCEMENT MATERIAL

CLINICAL AND RELATED TERMS

---

1. Amyelencephalia - absence of both brain and spinal cords.

2. Amyotrophy - atrophy of the spinal cord.

3. Apraxia - the loss of an ability to carry out normal familiar movements in the absence of sensory or motor impairment.

4. Arachnitis - inflammation of the arachnoid membrane.

5. Bradykinesia - an abnormal slowness of voluntary movements.

6. Carotid Angiography - the injection of dye into the carotid artery to visualize tumors.

7. Cephalalgia - headache

8. Chordotomy - division of the anterolateral tracts of the spinal cord.

9. Craniocele - herniation of any part of the cranial contents through a defect in the skull.

10. Duraplasty - plastic repair of the dura mater.

11. Electrocorticography - electroencephalography where the electrodes are applied directly to the cerebral cortex.

12. Encephalomalacia - morbid softening of the brain tissue.

13. Endarterectomy - the surgical removal of plaques within an extracranial artery, usually the carotid artery. Used to prevent strokes.

14. Hemiballismus - violent motor restlessness, usually of the upper extremities.

15. Hemispherectomy - resection of a cerebral hemisphere.

16. Hydromyelia - accumulation of fluid within the spinal cord. Central canal tends to enlarge.

17. Hypokinesia - abnormal decrease in motor function.

18. Leptomeningitis - an inflammation or infection of the arachnoid and pia mater of the brain and spinal cord.

19. Metrizamide - a nonionic, water-soluble, iodinated, radiographic contrast medium used in myelography and other techniques.

20. Microgyrus - an abnormally small, malformed convolution of the brain.

21. Migraine - a severe headache, usually involving one side of the head, that is often accompanied by nausea and vomiting.

22. Myelodysplasia - defective development of the spinal cord.

23. Myelography - the X-ray visualization of the spinal cord by means of a contrast medium, such as metrizamide into the subarachnoid space.

24. Pachymeningitis - inflammation of the dura mater.

25. RIND - reversible ischemic neurological effect.

26. TORCH - a symbolism used for remembering the most common prenatal infections: toxoplasmosis, other (syphilis, etc.), rubella, cytomegalovirus, and herpes.

27. Tractotomy - a cross section of a nerve tract in the CNS used for the relief of pain.

DISORDERS/HOMEOSTATIC IMBALANCES

Neoplasms

1. Gliosarcoma - a glioma combined with fusiform cells of a sarcoma.

2. Hemangioblastoma - a capillary hemangioma of the brain, consisting of proliferated blood vessel cells or angioblasts.

3. Medulloblastoma - a soft, infiltrating, malignant tumor, developing on the roof of the fourth ventricle and cerebellum. Tends to infiltrate the meninges.

4. Meningioma - a slow-growing tumor that originates in the arachnoid tissue.

Infectious Diseases

1. Bacterial Meningitis - a meningitis commonly caused by Hemophilus influenzae that affects children under the age of five. May be a part of the normal flora of adults. A vaccine is available for all children after the age of two.

2. Cryptococcosis - a disseminating systemic fungal infection caused by Cryptococcus neoformans that has a predilection for the brain and meninges.

3. Echinococcosis - a tapeworm infection caused by Echinococcus granulosis that forms hydatid cysts through the body of the host, including the brain and spinal cord.

4. Kuru - a chronic, progressive, usually-fatal disorder of the CNS, caused by a slow, unconventional virus. Seen only in the headhunting cannibalistic Fore indian tribes of New Guinea.

5. Rabies - an acute infectious disease of the CNS, caused by an RNA virus of the rhabdoviridae group. The virus is present in the host's saliva, with human infection occurring following a bite of a rabid animal. The virus appears to follow neural pathways, ultimately reaching the brain.

6. Tabes Dorsalis - sclerosis of the posterior columns of the spinal cord due to a syphilis infection of the CNS. Symptoms include postural instability and a staggering wide base gait.

7. Toxoplasmosis - a protozoan disease caused by Toxoplasma gondii that may affect neonates and children under two years. The congenital form is marked by CNS lesions that may lead to blindness, brain defects, and death. Commonly transmitted in the saliva and excrement of infected cats and rodents.

8. Waterhouse-Friderichsen Syndrome - the fulminating or malignant form of epidemic cerebrospinal meningitis, usually caused by Neisseria meningitidis. Usually marked by sudden onset and short course, with high fever, coma, collapse, cyanosis, and severe hemorrhages of the skin.

Genetic and Developmental Disorders

1. Arnold-Chiari Malformation - an unusual congenital anomaly, usually associated with hydrocephalus, where the cerebellum and medulla protrude down the cervical spinal canal through the foramen magnum.

2. Friedreich's Ataxia - a hereditary sclerosis of the lateral and dorsal column of the spinal cord, usually appearing in early childhood, characterized by ataxia, speech impairment, scoliosis, muscular paralysis and other features.

3. Wilson's Disease - a rare, progressive, inherited disorder due to an inability to properly metabolize copper, resulting in accumulations in the brain, liver, cornea, and other tissues. Neurological symptoms most commonly occur in young adults.

Degenerative Disorders

1. Subacute Sclerosing Panencephalitis (SSP) - an encephalitis that usually occurs in young children and is characterized by a progressive intellectual deterioration, behavioral disorders, and involuntary muscular disorders. May be due to a viral infection.

2. Progressive Multifocal Leukoencephalopathy (PML) - a rare, demyelinating disorder that primarily affects middle-aged patients with some form of neoplastic or immunocompromising disorder. The disease appears to be caused by the JC virus or SV 40 virus, that affects the white matter of the brain, brain stem, and cerebellum.

APPLIED PHARMACOLOGY

Drugs for Brain Edema and Bleeding

1. Dexamethasone (Decadron, Dexone, Hexadrol) - used to reduce or prevent cerebral edema, associated with surgical and other brain trauma, cerebral vascular accidents, and brain malignancies. Appears to depress brain inflammation.

2. Mannitol (Osmitrol) - used to rapidly reduce cerebral edema. Acts as an obligatory osmotic diuretic and is the drug of choice for rapid reduction of intracranial pressure.

3. Epsilon-Aminocaproic Acid (Amicar) - used to prevent recurrent subarachnoid hemorrhaging immediately following an acute bleed. Agent is a potent competitive inhibitor of plasminogen activators.

Drugs for Severe Headaches

1. Ergotamine Tartrate (Cafergot, Ercaf, Wigraine) - used in the treatment of pain of migraine and other headaches by dilated blood vessels. Will not prevent headaches. Acts to constrict blood vessels in the head.

2. Methysergide (Sansert) - used in the prophylaxis of migraine and cluster headaches. Appears to act in the CNS by sero- tonin agonism at presynaptic autonomic receptors and/or post-synaptic receptors.

3. Amitriptyline (Elavil) - used in the prevention of migraine and cluster headaches. As a tricyclic antidepressant, it appears to block the reuptake of serotonin at central synapses.

4. Propanolol (Inderal) - used as the drug of choice for migraine prophylaxis. Action may be related to inhibition of release of serotonin centrally.

Drugs for Tension Headaches

1. Butalbital-ASA-Caffeine (Fiorinal) - used for tension headaches, reduction of anxiety, and to relieve insomnia. May act to partially block nerve impulses at nerve cell connections.

2. Tabutal - used for tension headaches and the reduction of anxiety. Acts similar to butalbital.

SUGGESTED READINGS

1. Angier, N. "Storming the Wall." Discover 11 (May, 1990):60-67.

2. Begley, S., J. Carey, and R. Sawhill. "How the Brain Works." Newsweek 7 (Feb. 1983).

3. Bower, B. "Inside the Autistic Brain." Science News 130 (Sept. 1986):154-155.

4. Bower, B. "The Language of the Brain." Science News 132 (July 1987):40-41.

5. Cowan, W.M. "The Development of the Brain." Scientific American 241 (Sept. 1979):112-133.

6. Fine, A. "Transplantation in the CNS." Scientific American 255 (Aug. 1986):52-58.

7. Galaburda, A.M., et al. "Right-Left Asymmetries in the Brain." Science 199 (1978):852.

8. Geschwind, N. "Specializations of the Human Brain." Scientific American 241 (Sept. 1979):180-199.

9. Gluhbegovic, N., and T.H. Williams. The Human Brain: A Photographic Guide. New York:Harper & Row, 1980.

10. Goldberger, A.L., D.R. Rigney, and B.J. West "Chaos and Fractals in Human Physiology." Scientific American @^@ (Feb. 1990):43-49.

11. Goldstein, G.W., and A.L. Betz. "The Blood-Brain Barrier." Scientific American 255 (Sept. 1986):74-83.

12. Guillemin, R. "Peptides in the Brain." Science 202 (1978):390.

13. Holloway, M. Profile: Vive la Difference." Scientific American 263 (Oct, 1990):40-42.

14. Hubel, D.H. "The Brain." Scientific American (Sept. 1979).

15. Iversen, L.L. "The Chemistry of the Brain." Scientific American 241 (Sept. 1979):134-149.

16. Johnson, G.T. "Is Spinal Anesthesia Best for You?" Mayo Clinic Health Letter (Oct. 1984).

17. Kety, S.S. "Disorders of the Human Brain." Scientific American 241 (Sept. 1979):202-214.

18. Krieger, D.T. "Brain Peptides: What, Where, and Why." Science 222 (1983):975.

19. Miller, J.A. "Sex Differences Found in Human Brains." Science News 126 (July 1984).

20. Miller, J.A. "Sex in the Spinal Cord." Science News 118 (Nov. 1980):329.

21. Nathanson, J.A., and P. Greengard. "Second Messenger in the Brain." Scientific American 237 (Aug. 1977):108-119.

22. Nauta, J.H., and M. Feirtag. "The Organization of the Brain." Scientific American (Sept. 1979).

23. Pajk, M., et al. "Alzheimer's Disease." American Journal of Nursing 84 (Feb. 1984):215-232.

24. Romero, J.H. "The Critical Minutes After Spinal Cord Injury." RN (Apr. 1988):61-67.

25. Routenberg, A. "The Reward System of the Brain." Scientific American 239 (Nov. 1978):154-164.

26. Silberner, J. "Alzheimer's Disease: Source Searching." Science News 128 (July 1985):24.

27. Spector, R. and C.E. Johnson. "The Mammalian Choroid Plexus." Scientific American 261 (Nov. 1989):68-74.

28. Springer, S.P., and G. Deutsch. Left Brain, Right Brain. San Francisco:W.H. Freeman, 1981.

29. Tangley, L . "Female Brain Anatomy May Differ." Science News 136 (Nov. 1989):

30. Thompson, R.F. The Brain: An Introduction to Neuroscience. New York:W.H. Freeman and Co., 1985.

31. Vellutino, F.R. "Dyslexia." Scientific American 256 (Mar. 1987):34-41.

32. Weiss, R. "Neurons Regenerate Into Spinal Cord." Science News 132 (Nov. 1987).

33. Weiss, R. "Women's Skills Linked to Estrogen Levels." Science News 134 (Nov. 1988):341.

34. Weiss, R. "New Therapies Brighten Stroke Horizon." Science News 136 (Nov. 1989):292.

35. Wurtman, R.J. "Alzheimer's Disease." Scientific American (Jan. 1985).

HANDOUTS

The following section contains prepared handout material which may be photocopied and distributed to the class. All materials are organized so that selected items can be cut and pasted for the instructors individual needs.

If budgets are a limiting factor in the use of handouts, these masters may be placed on reserve in the library for students to photocopy at their convenience.

Preview Of Selected Key Terms

Central Nervous System . . . . The brain and spinal cord.

Brain ventricle . . . . (ventr=hollow cavity) Fluid filled cavity of the brain.

Cerebrum . . . . The cerebral hemispheres.

Brain stem . . . . Collevtively the midbrain, pons and medulla of the brain.

Cerebral cortex . . . . The outer gray matter region of the cerebral hemispheres.

Cerebellum . . . . Brain region most involved in producing smooth, coordinated skeletal muscle activity.

Basal (cerebral) nuclei . . . . Gray matter areas located deep within the white matter of the cerebral hemispheres.

Limbic system . . . . (limbus=ring) Functional brain system involved in emotional response.

Reticular formation . . . . Functional system that spans the brain stem; involved in regulating sensory input to the cerebral cortex, cortical arousal, and control of motor behavior.

Choroid plexus . . . . (plex=interweaving) A capillary knot that protrudes into a brain ventricle; involved in forming cerebrospinal fluid.

Meninges . . . . (mening=membrane) Protective coverings of the CNS; from the most external to the most internal, the dura mater, arachnoid, and pia mater.

Cerebrospinal fluid . . . . Plasmalike fluid that fills tha cavities of the CNS and surrounds the CNS externally; protects the brain and spinal cord.

Terms/Disorders

1. Bacterial Meningitis - a meningitis commonly caused by Hemophilus influenzae that affects children under the age of five. May be a part of the normal flora of adults. A vaccine is available for all children after the age of two.

2. Butalbital-ASA-Caffeine (Fiorinal) - used for tension headaches, reduction of anxiety, and to relieve insomnia. May act to partially block nerve impulses at nerve cell connections.

3. Carotid Angiography - the injection of dye into the carotid artery to visualize tumors.

4. Cryptococcosis - a disseminating systemic fungal infection caused by Cryptococcus neoformans that has a predilection for the brain and meninges.

5. Echinococcosis - a tapeworm infection caused by Echinococcus granulosis that forms hydatid cysts through the body of the host, including the brain and spinal cord.

6. Gliosarcoma - a glioma combined with fusiform cells of a sarcoma.

7. Hypokinesia - abnormal decrease in motor function.

8. Kuru - a chronic, progressive, usually-fatal disorder of the CNS, caused by a slow, unconventional virus. Seen only in the headhunting cannibalistic Fore indian tribes of New Guinea.

9. Leptomeningitis - an inflammation or infection of the arachnoid and pia mater of the brain and spinal cord.

10. Meningioma - a slow-growing tumor that originates in the arachnoid tissue.

11. Migraine - a severe headache, usually involving one side of the head, that is often accompanied by nausea and vomiting.

12. Propanolol (Inderal) - used as the drug of choice for migraine prophylaxis. Action may be related to inhibition of release of serotonin centrally.

13. Rabies - an acute infectious disease of the CNS, caused by an RNA virus of the rhabdoviridae group. The virus is present in the host's saliva, with human infection occurring following a bite of a rabid animal. The virus appears to follow neural pathways, ultimately reaching the brain.

14. Subacute Sclerosing Panencephalitis (SSP) - an encephalitis that usually occurs in young children and is characterized by a progressive intellectual deterioration, behavioral disorders, and involuntary muscular disorders. May be due to a viral infection.

15. Tabutal - used for tension headaches and the reduction of anxiety. Acts similar to butalbital.

16. Toxoplasmosis - a protozoan disease caused by Toxoplasma gondii that may affect neonates and children under two years. The congenital form is marked by CNS lesions that may lead to blindness, brain defects, and death. Commonly transmitted in the saliva and excrement of infected cats and rodents.

17. TORCH - a symbolism used for remembering the most common prenatal infections: toxoplasmosis, other (syphilis, etc.), rubella, cytomegalovirus, and herpes.

BLACK LINE MASTERS

The following section contains selected unlabeled line art representations of key elements in this chapter. These diagrams may be utilized in several ways depending on individual needs:

1. Photocopy directly onto acetate film for overhead projection during class lecture/discussion. The art is unlabeled so that the instructor may write directly on the acetate during class and emphasize critical features. A key advantage in the use of this form of visual presentation is the ease with which students are able to comprehend complex anatomical and physiological relationships presented during class.

2. Photocopy for handouts so that the students may take notes directly on the diagrams and in that way have a clear understanding of the relationship between the figure and lecture material.

3. If the course is on a tight budget, place masters of diagrams on reserve (usually in a notebook in the library) for students to make copies should they choose to do so.

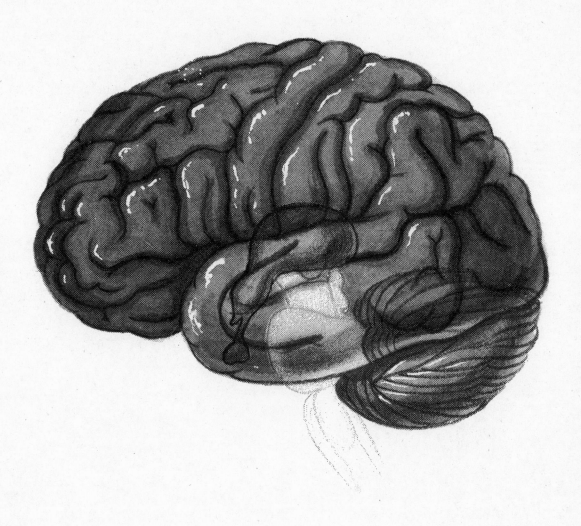

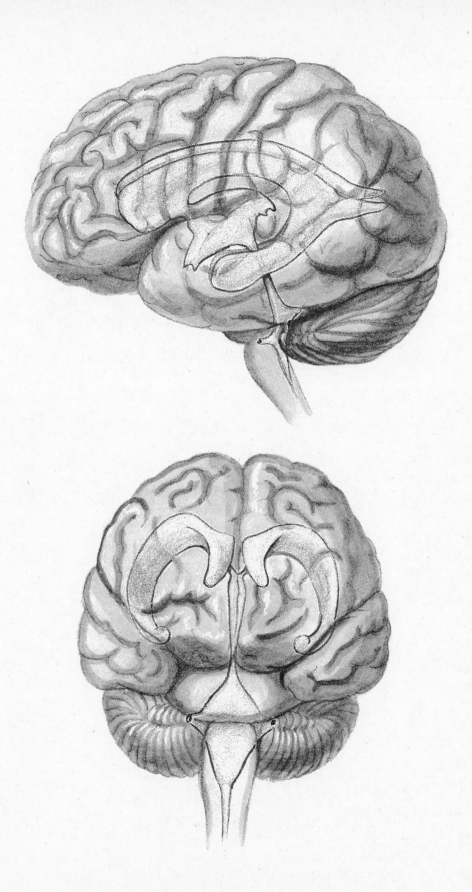

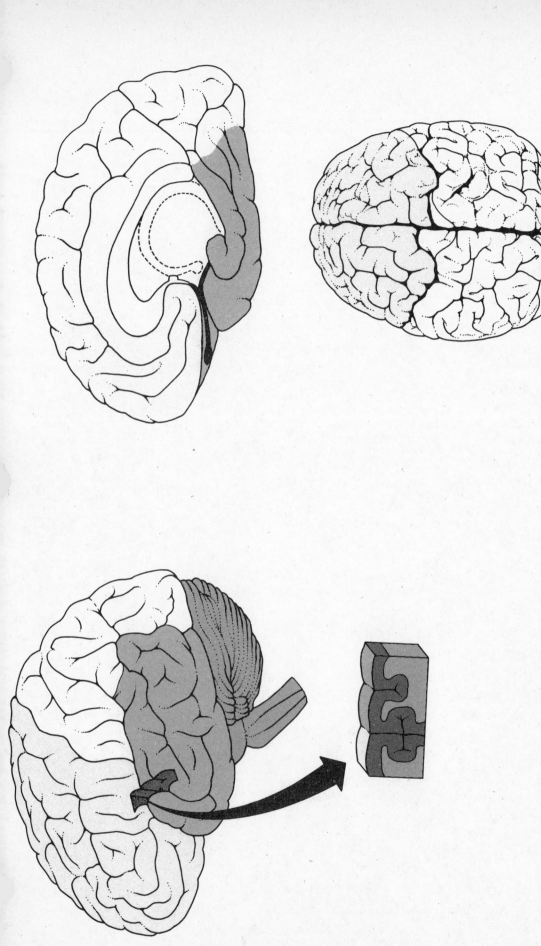

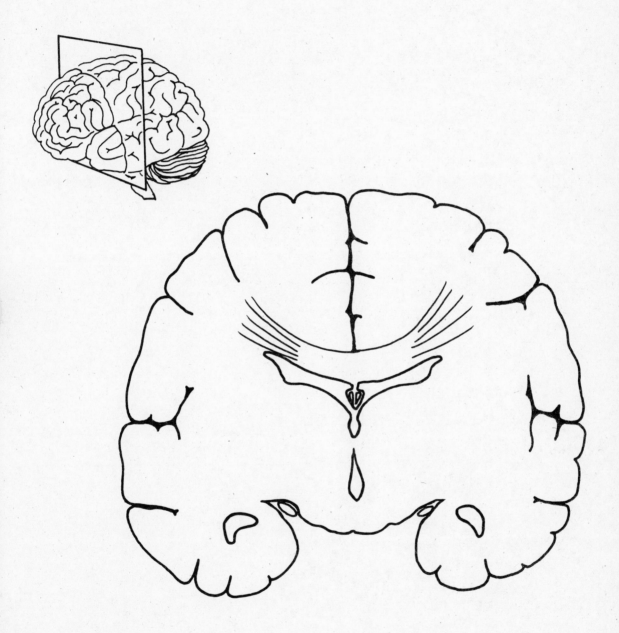

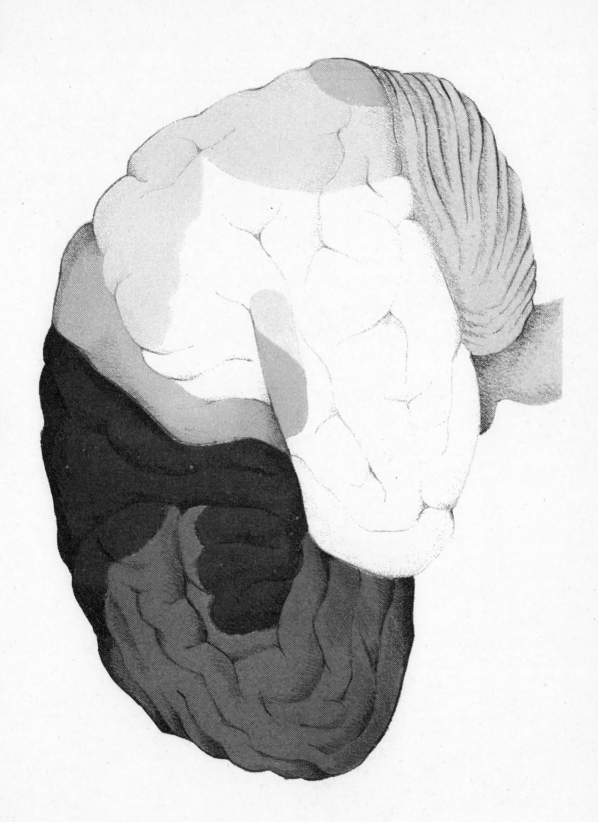

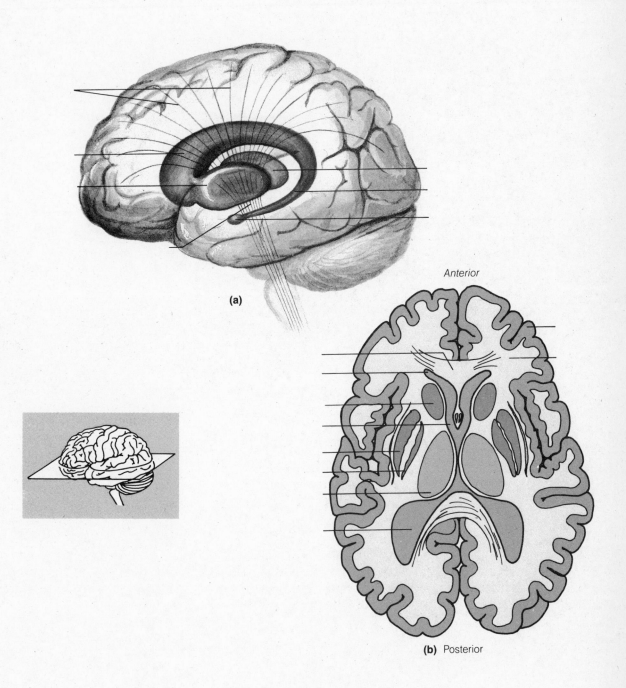

(a)

Anterior

(b) Posterior

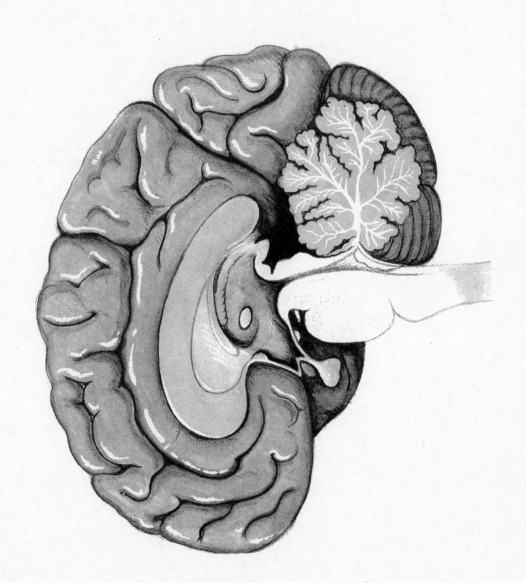

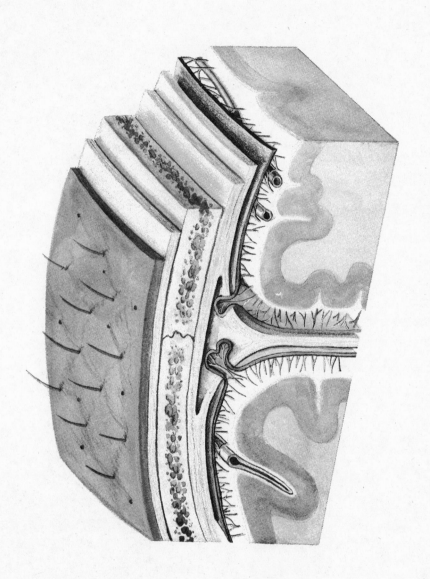

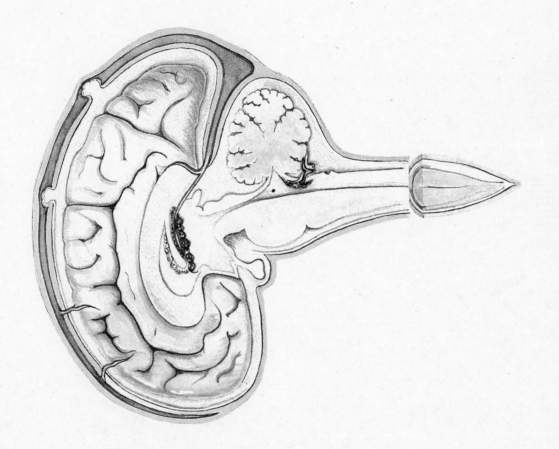

Cervical
spinal nerves

Cervical
enlargement

Dura
and
arachnoid
mater

Thoracic
spinal nerves

Lumbar
enlargement

Conus
medullaris

Cauda
equina

Lumbar
spinal nerves

Sacral
spinal
nerves

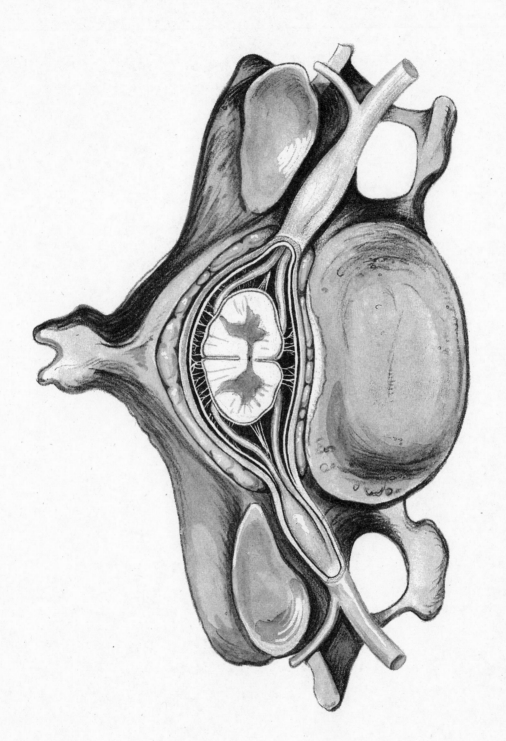

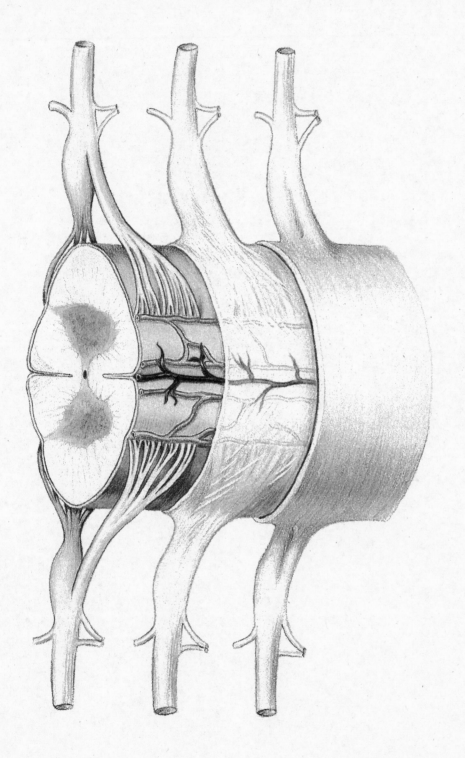

Test Bank

MATCHING QUESTIONS

Match the following:

a. Frontal
b. Parietal

c. Occipital
d. Temporal

___ 1. Auditory area.
___ 2. Primary sensory cortex.
___ 3. Somatic motor cortex.
___ 4. Motor speech area.
___ 5. Premotor area.
___ 6. Seat of intelligence, abstract reasoning.
___ 7. Visual areas.
___ 8. Language/speech comprehension area.
___ 9. Taste (gustatory) area.

Qtype:»Memory   Outline:»II.D.2.   Text pp.»383-389
Answers:»1-d; 2-b; 3-a; 4-a; 5-a; 6-a; 7-c; 8-d; 9-b

Match the following:

a. Ventricles
b. Dura mater
c. Arachnoid villi
d. Central canal
e. Arachnoid

f. Choroid plexuses
g. Subarachnoid space
h. Pia mater
i. Meningitis
j. Hydrocephalus

___ 1. The innermost layer of the meninges, delicate, contains many blood vessels.
___ 2. The weblike, spidery middle meningeal layer.
___ 3. Inflammation of the brain coverings that may be due to pathogenic bacteria.
___ 4. Normally, the cerebrospinal fluid flows freely from the ventricle, then into the
         _____.
___ 5. The cerebrospinal fluid helps to protect the brain and cord against shock. It is
         filtered into the ventricles through_____.
___ 6. The cerebrospinal fluid is returned to the blood in the venous sinuses through
         projections called _____.
___ 7. Any obstruction to the normal flow of cerebrospinal fluid within the brain may
         give rise to a condition called _____.

Qtype:»Memory   Outline:»II.C.   Text pp.»381-382
Answers:»1-h; 2-e; 3-i; 4-g; 5-f; 6-c; 7-j

Match the following:
  a. Fasciculi gracilis
  b. Corticospinal tract
  c. Rubrospinal tract
  d. Anterior spinothalamic tract
  e. Posterior spinocerebellar tract
  ___ 1. Impulses arise in proprioceptors, ascend the cord via this tract and terminate in the cerebellum.
  ___ 2. Transmits impulses for crude touch and pressure to the opposite side of the brain.
  ___ 3. Descending (pyramidal) tract originating with large cells of the motor cortex. Major motor supply for musculature of the limbs.
  ___ 4. Important efferent pathway of the extrapyramidal system. Transmits impulses concerned with muscle tone to skeletal muscles of the opposite side of the body.

  Qtype:»Memory   Outline:»III.C.2.   Text pp.»409-413
  Answers:»1-e; 2-d; 3-b; 4-c

Match the area to the following descriptions:
  a. Somatosensory area   e. Premotor area
  b. Gnostic area   f. Thalamus
  c. Prefrontal   g. Medulla
  d. Primary motor cortex   h. Hypothalamus
  ___ 1. A major relay station for sensory information ascending to primary sensory areas of the cerebral cortex. Contains many specialized nuclei.
  ___ 2. This brain area associates experiences necessary for the production of abstract ideas, judgment, and conscience.
  ___ 3. The axons from this area form the major pyramidal tracts.
  ___ 4. The site of reception and integration of information from sensory association areas to produce one common integrated thought, and activates other parts of the cortex to produce an appropriate response.
  ___ 5. This area is the main visceral control center of the body.

  Qtype:»Memory   Outline:»II   Text pp.»379-407
  Answers:»1-f; 2-c; 3-d; 4-b; 5-h

TRUE/FALSE QUESTIONS

1. The visual sensory area of the cerebral cortex is located in the occipital lobe.
                a. true   b. false

  Qtype:»Memory   Outline:»II.D.2.d.   Text pp.»387
  Answers:»true

2. The motor cortex is located in the precentral gyrus of the frontal lobe.
                a. true   b. false

  Qtype:»Memory   Outline:»II.D.2.c.   Text pp.»385
  Answers:»true

3. A functional center found within the cerebellum is a respiratory center involved in the control or the rate and depth of breathing.

        a. true   b. false

Qtype:»Memory   Outline:»II.G.1.   Text pp.»398-399
Answers:»false

---

4. Cell bodies of the motor neurons of the spinal nerves are located in the anterior horn of the spinal cord.

        a. true   b. false

Qtype:»Memory   Outline:»III.C.2.   Text pp.»409
Answers:»true

---

5. Meningitis is the most accurate term for inflammation of neurons.

        a. true   b. false

Qtype:»Memory   Outline:»II.I.2.   Text pp.»403
Answers:»false

---

6. The spinal cord ends at the level of T-12.

        a. true   b. false

Qtype:»Memory   Outline:»III.A.2.   Text pp.»407
Answers:»false

---

7. Basal (cerebral) nuclei are gray matter areas buried deep within the white matter of the cerebellum.

        a. true   b. false

Qtype:»Memory   Outline:»II.D.4.   Text pp.»392
Answers:»false

---

8. Difficulty in breathing may reflect damage to respiratory centers located in the medulla and pons.

        a. true   b. false

Qtype:»Memory   Outline:»II.F.   Text pp.»397-398
Answers:»true

---

9. Cerebrospinal fluid circulates within the ventricles of the brain and in the subarachnoid space outside the brain.

        a. true   b. false

Qtype:»Memory   Outline:»II.I.3.c.   Text pp.»404
Answers:»true

---

10. The first obvious sign that the nervous system is forming in the embryo is the thickening of the surface endoderm to form the neural plate.

                a. true   b. false

Qtype:»Concept   Outline:»II.A.1.   Text pp.»379
Answers:»false

---

11. The dominant cerebral hemisphere is usually the right.

                a. true   b. false

Qtype:»Memory   Outline:»II.D.2.f.   Text pp.»389
Answers:»false

---

12. The limbic system acts as our emotional or affective brain.

                a. true   b. false

Qtype:»Memory   Outline:»II.H.1.c.   Text pp.»400
Answers:»true

---

13. A part of the diencephalon structure is formed by the hypothalamus.

                a. true   b. false

Qtype:»Memory   Outline:»II.A.3.b.   Text pp.»380
Answers:»true

---

14. One of the major functions of the pons is to regulate the endocrine system by producing releasing factors that control the function of the anterior pituitary.

                a. true   b. false

Qtype:»Concept   Outline:»II.F.2.b.   Text pp.»396
Answers:»false

---

15. The medulla is anatomically associated with cranial nerves 9, 10, and 11.

                a. true   b. false

Qtype:»Memory   Outline:»II.F.3.   Text pp.»398
Answers:»true

---

16. The canal connecting the third and fourth ventricles and running through the midbrain is the foramen of Monro.

                a. true   b. false

Qtype:»Memory   Outline:»II.C.   Text pp.»381-382
Answers:»false

---

17. The term "central nervous system" refers to the brain, spinal cord, and peripheral nerves.
        a. true   b. false

Qtype:»Concept   Outline:»I.   Text pp.»378
Answers:»false

18. Motor impulses from the cortex always originate in the occipital lobe.
        a. true   b. false

Qtype:»Concept   Outline:»II.D.2.c   Text pp.»385
Answers:»false

19. Sorting of sensory information and relaying it to the appropriate cerebral sensory area occurs in the thalamus.
        a. true   b. false

Qtype:»Concept   Outline:»II.E.1.   Text pp.»392
Answers:»true

20. Commissural fibers form the corpus striatum.
        a. true   b. false

Qtype:»Memory   Outline:»II.D.3.a.   Text pp.»391
Answers:»false

21. The third ventricle is found in the diencephalon.
        a. true   b. false

Qtype:»Memory   Outline:»II.C.2.   Text pp.»382
Answers:»true

22. The cerebral hemispheres of the brain develop from the prosencephalon.
        a. true   b. false

Qtype:»Memory   Outline:»II.A.2.   Text pp.»380
Answers:»true

23. MRI scans seem to reveal tumors in the posterior cranial fossa and multiple sclerosis plaques better than CAT scans.
        a. true   b. false

Qtype:»Concept   Outline:»IV.C.2.   Text pp.»417
Answers:»true

24. In order to visualize the ventricles of the brain, it would be useful to order a cerebral angiogram.

        a. true   b. false

Qtype:»Concept   Outline:»IV.A.   Text pp.»417
Answers:»false

24. Embryonic damage to the mesencephalon could result in improper formation of the midbrain.

        a. true   b. false

Qtype:»Concept   Outline:»II.A.3.e.   Text pp.»380
Answers:»true

26. A disturbance of posture, muscle tremors at rest, and uncontrolled muscle contraction are all symptoms of damage to the basal nuclei.

        a. true   b. false

Qtype:»Memory   Outline:»II.D.4.a.   Text pp.»392
Answers:»true

27. "Jet lag," which affects our biological clock, could be related to pineal gland function.

        a. true   b. false

Qtype:»Concept   Outline:»II.E.3.a.   Text pp.»394
Answers:»true

28. Most of the ascending and descending pathways to and from the brain, cross over from one side of the spinal cord to the other.

        a. true   b. false

Qtype:»Concept   Outline:»III.C.2.   Text pp.»411
Answers:»true

29. Spinocerebellar tracts convey motor information from the cerebellum to motor nerve cells in the spinal cord.

        a. true   b. false

Qtype:»Concept   Outline:»III.C.2.c.   Text pp.»411
Answers:»false

30. Extrapyramidal tracts are always afferent.

        a. true   b. false

Qtype:»Concept   Outline:»III.C.2.d.   Text pp.»414
Answers:»false

MULTIPLE-CHOICE QUESTIONS

1. Which of the following are involved with motor activity (either initiation or coordination)?
   a. precentral gyrus
   b. cerebellum
   c. basal nuclei
   d. red nuclei
   e. All of the above are involved.

   Qtype:»Memory   Outline:»II.   Text pp.»397-407
   Answers:»e

---

2. The blood brain barrier inhibits passage of:
   a. glucose.
   b. water.
   c. lipid soluble substances.
   d. sodium ions.
   e. urea and creatine.

   Qtype:»Memory   Outline:»II.I.4.   Text pp.»405
   Answers:»e

---

3. Nuclei of cranial nerves V, VI, VII are found in the:
   a. midbrain.
   b. medulla.
   c. pons.
   d. cerebrum.

   Qtype:»Memory   Outline:»II.F.2.   Text pp.»398
   Answers:»c

---

4. Which of the following is **not** part of the basal nuclei?
   a. putamen
   b. lentiform nucleus
   c. globus pallidus
   d. substantia nigra

   Qtype:»Memory   Outline:»II.D.4.   Text pp.»392
   Answers:»d

---

5. All of the following are stuctures of the limbic system except:
   a. hippocampus.
   b. cingulate gyrus.
   c. amygdaloid nucleus.
   d. hypothalamus.
   e. caudate nucleus.

   Qtype:»Memory   Outline:»II.H.1.   Text pp.»400
   Answers:»e

---

6. Which of the following is **not** a midbrain structure?
   a. third ventricle
   b. cerebral peduncles
   c. corpora quadrigemina
   d. red nucleus

   Qtype:»Memory   Outline:»II.F.1.   Text pp.»398
   Answers:»a

---

7. Which of the following is **not** a hindbrain structure?
    a. fourth ventricle
    b. pons
    c. medulla
    d. cerebral nuclei

    Qtype:»Memory   Outline:»II.A.2.c.   Text pp.»380
    Answers:»d

8. The arbor vitae concerns:
    a. cerebellar grey matter.
    b. cerebellar white matter.
    c. the pleatlike convolutions of the cerebellum.
    d. floculonodular nodes.

    Qtype:»Memory · Outline:»II.G.1.e.   Text pp.»399
    Answers:»b

9. White matter (myelinated fibers) is found in all the following locations, with the exception of:
    a. corpus callosum.
    b. cerebral cortex.
    c. corticospinal tracts.
    d. the outer surface of the spinal cord.

    Qtype:»Concept   Outline:»II.D.3.   Text pp.»391
    Answers:»b

10. The brain stem consists of:
    a. cerebrum, pons, midbrain, and medulla.
    b. midbrain, medulla, and pons.
    c. pons, medulla, cerebullum, and midbrain.
    d. midbrain only.

    Qtype:»Memory   Outline:»II.F.   Text pp.»395
    Answers:»b

11. The primary auditory cortex is located in the:
    a. prefrontal lobe.
    b. frontal lobe.
    c. temporal lobe.
    d. parietal lobe.
    e. occipital lobe.

    Qtype:»Memory   Outline:»II.D.2.d.   Text pp.»387
    Answers:»c

12. The spinal cord has grey matter on the:
    a. outside, white matter on the inside and a dorsal motor root.
    b. inside, white matter on the outside and a ventral motor root.
    c. inside, white matter on the outside and a dorsal motor root.
    d. outside, white matter on the inside and a ventral motor root.

    Qtype:»Memory   Outline:»III.C.   Text pp.»409-414
    Answers:»b

13. The subarachnoid space lies between what two layers of meninges?
    a. arachnoid   c. arachnoid and dura
    b. arachnoid and pia   d. dura and epidura

    Qtype:»Memory   Outline:»III.A.2.   Text pp.»407
    Answers:»b

14. The brain area that regulates activities that control the state of wakefulness or alertness of
    the cerebral cortex is the:
    a. thalamus.   c. pyramids.
    b. reticular formation.   d. limbic system.

    Qtype:»Memory   Outline:»II.H.2   Text pp.»402
    Answers:»b

15. The vital centers for the control of heart rate, respiration, and blood pressure are located in:
    a. the pons.   c. the midbrain.
    b. the medulla.   d. the cerebrum.

    Qtype:»Memory   Outline:»II.F.3.   Text pp.»398
    Answers:»b

16. Cell bodies of the sensory neurons of the spinal nerves are located in:
    a. the dorsal root ganglia of the spinal cord.
    b. the ventral root ganglia of the cord.
    c. the thalamus.
    d. sympathetic ganglia.

    Qtype:»Memory   Outline:»III.C.1.d.   Text pp.»409
    Answers:»a

17. The fissure separating the cerebral hemispheres is the:
    a. central fissure.   c. parieto-occipital fissure.
    b. longitudinal fissure.   d. lateral fissure.

    Qtype:»Memory   Outline:»II.D.1.c.   Text pp.»382
    Answers:»b

18. Which of the following would you **not** find in normal cerebrospinal fluid?
    a. glucose
    b. red blood cells

    c. potassium
    d. protein

Qtype:»Concept   Outline:»II.I.3.a.   Text pp.»404
Answers:»b

19. Mr. J.H. was injured in an accident that completely severed his spinal cord at the level of T-12. You would expect to find all the following <u>except</u>:
    a. paralysis of the upper extremities.
    b. loss of sensation below the level of injury.
    c. slurred speech.
    d. perspiration in affected area.

Qtype:»Application Outline:»III.D.1.   Text pp.»416
Answers:»b

20. Injury to the hypothalamus may result in all the following <u>except</u>:
    a. pathologic sleep.
    b. loss of body temperature control.
    c. production of excessive quantities of urine.
    d. loss of proprioception.
    e. control of endocrine function.

Qtype:»Concept   Outline:»II.E.2.d.   Text pp.»394
Answers:»d

21. The tough, leathery meningeal layer is the:
    a. dura mater.
    b. subarachnoid.

    c. arachnoid.
    d. pia mater.

Qtype:»Memory   Outline:»II.I.2.a.   Text pp.»402
Answers:»a

22. A shallow groove on the surface of the cortex is called a:
    a. sulcus.
    b. fissure.
    c. gyrus.

    d. furrow.
    e. map.

Qtype:»Memory   Outline:»II.D.1.b.   Text pp.»382
Answers:»a

23. The cerebrospinal fluid
    a. is secreted by the arachnoid villi.
    b. enters the four ventricles after filling and circulating through the sub-arachnoid space.
    c. is secreted mostly by the ependymal cells lining the brain ventricles.
    d. is formed mostly by the choroid plexuses.

    Qtype:»Memory   Outline:»II.I.3.b.   Text pp.»404
    Answers:»d

24. Which of the following is true concerning the development of the nervous system after
    birth?
    a. The hypothalamus is the last CNS structure to mature.
    b. Anencephaly is normally easily corrected.
    c. Most people, after age 65 are actually exhibiting signs of true senility.
    d. All of the above are false.

    Qtype:»Concept   Outline:»V.C.   Text pp.»419
    Answers:»a

25. If the posterior of the neural tube failed to develop properly:
    a. the spinal cord may be affected.
    b. the cranial nerves would not form.
    c. the hind brain would not be present.
    d. the telencephalon would cease development.

    Qtype:»Concept   Outline:»II.A.1.c.   Text pp.»380
    Answers:»a

26. The central sulcus separates which lobes?
    a. frontal from parietal   c. temporal from parietal
    b. parietal from occipital   d. frontal from temporal

    Qtype:»Memory   Outline:»II.D.1.d.   Text pp.»382
    Answers:»a

27. Neural tracts that convey life saving information to the brain concerning burning pain
    would be:
    a. anterior spinothalamic.   c. lateral spinothalamic.
    b. reticulospinal.   d. posterior spinothalamic.

    Qtype:»Concept   Outline:»III.C.2.c.   Text pp.»412
    Answers:»c

28. Which of the following generalizations is/are correct about cerebral cortex function?
    1. Each hemisphere is concerned with sensory and motor function of the opposite side.
    2. There is lateralization of cortical function.
    3. Sensory and motor areas of the cortex act alone, independently from each other.
    a. 1 only
    b. 2 only
    c. 3 only
    d. 1 and 2
    e. 2 and 3

    Qtype:»Memory   Outline:»II.D.2.b.   Text pp.»384
    Answers:»d

29. The hypothalamus:
    a. is the thermostat of the body since it regulates temperature.
    b. is thought to be the center for psychosomatic illness.
    c. contains feeding and hunger centers.
    d. contains neurons sensitive to the solute concentration of the blood.
    e. All the above are correct.

    Qtype:»Concept   Outline:»II.E.2.d.   Text pp.»394
    Answers:»e

30. The cerebellum:
    1. receives information from the cerebral motor cortex and body proprioceptors.
    2. assesses incoming information and calculates the optimum coordination of muscle activity.
    3. sends the "blueprint" for muscle coordination to the motor cortex.
    a. 1 only
    b. 1 and 2
    c. 1 and 3
    d. 2 and 3
    e. 1, 2 and 3

    Qtype:»Concept   Outline:»II.G.2.   Text pp.»400
    Answers:»e

31. Injury to the brain by any cause may lead to a localized breakdown of the blood-brain barrier. Which of the following is most likely a direct cause of breakdown?
    1. destruction of endothelial cells
    2. modification of tight junctions
    3. loss of astrocytes as the forming cell of the barrier
    a. 1 only
    b. 2 only
    c. 3 only
    d. 1 and 2
    e. 2 and 3

    Qtype:»Concept   Outline:»II.1.4.   Text pp.»405
    Answers:»d

32. Which of the following is true of homeostatic imbalances of the brain?
    a. A concussion is severe brain damage in which the victim is dizzy and may "see stars".
    b. A blow to the head may be fatal due to the formation of epidural hematomas.
    c. Cerebrovascular accident always involves rupturing central nervous system blood vessels.
    d. PET scans of Alzheimers patients show high glucose concentrations in the cerebral cortex.
    e. Multiple sclerosis is possibly a virally induced autoimmune problem.

    Qtype:»Memory   Outline:»II.J.1.   Text pp.»406
    Answers:»e

33. The spinal cord develops from the:
    a. caudal portion of the neural tube.
    b. sulcus limitans.
    c. basal plate.
    d. anterior part of the embryonic neural tube.
    e. alar palte.

    Qtype:»Memory   Outline:»III.B.   Text pp.»408
    Answers:»a

34. White matter of the spinal cord:
    a. is composed of both myelinated and unmyelinated fibers.
    b. ascends to higher CNS centers.
    c. descends to lower levels.
    d. runs from one side of the spinal cord to the other.
    e. All the above are correct.

    Qtype:»Memory   Outline:»III.C.2.   Text pp.»409
    Answers:»e

35. Which of the following stimuli will cause an individual to perceive a high temperature sensation from a specific body area (eg. fingertip)?
    1. application of heat to a thermoreceptor in the fingertip.
    2. electrical stimulation of a sensory neuron in the thermal perception circuit.
    3. electrically stimulate the descending neural pathway that innervates that area.
    a. 1 only   d. 1 and 3
    b. 2 only   e. 1, 2 and 3
    c. 1 and 2

    Qtype:»Concept   Outline:»III.C.2.c.   Text pp.»414
    Answers:»c

36. An individual accidentally transected the spinal cord between T-11 and L-1. We would call this problem:
    a. paraplegia
    b. hemiplegia
    c. quadraplegia
    d. None of the above.

> Qtype:»Concept   Outline:»III.D.3.   Text pp.»416
> Answers:»a

37. Which of the following does **not** belong with the rest?
    a. rubrospinal.
    b. vestibulospinal
    c. corticospinal
    d. reticulospinal
    e. tectospinal

> Qtype:»Memory   Outline:»III.C.2.d.   Text pp.»414
> Answers:»c

SHORT-ANSWER QUESTIONS

1. What is the importance of the fact that the outer portion of the cerebral hemispheres is convoluted?

> Qtype:»Concept   Outline:»II.D.2.   Text pp.»383
> Answers:»The cerebral cortex is only 2-4 mm thick, howeer, the convolutions effectively triple the cortical surface area. As a result, the cortex accounts for 40% of the total brain mass.

2. What is the cauda equina and why was it given this name?

> Qtype:»Concept   Outline:»III.A.6.   Text pp.»407
> Answers:»The causa equina is a collection of nerve roots at the inferior end of the vertebral canal and is given this name because of its resemblance to a horse's tail. This arrangement reflects the different rates of growth between the vertebral column and spinal cord. Because the column grows more rapidly than the cord, the lower nerves must "chase" to their exit points inferiorly thus forming cauda equina.

3. Describe the cause of hydrocephalus and explain why this condition is much more serious in adults than in newborns.

> Qtype:»Concept   Outline:»II.I.3.   Text pp.»405
> Answers:»Hydrocephaly refers to a blockage of the normal circulation and drainage of CSF throughout the meninges and ventricles. If allowed to accululate, excessive pressure could be exerted on the brain. In newborns, the fontanels allow the skull to enlarge, while in adults, the cranial bones are fused and no expansion is possible.

CLINICAL QUESTIONS

1. Six-year old Jimmy is confined to a wheelchair. He frequently drools and his limbs hang limply in strange angular positions. His diagnosis is cerebral palsy. Name several (possible) causes of cerebral palsy.

   > Qtype:»Application Outline:»V.B.   Text pp.»417
   > Answers:»Cerebral palsy may be due to a lack of oxygen at birth, or may be due to a viral infection, excessive smoking by the mother, radiation, drugs, or alcohol. The disorder is a neuromuscular disability in which the voluntary muscles are poorly controlled or paralyzed.

2. Stacy was involved in a car accident which caused her head to snap forward and backward forcefully. Although no external signs of injury were seen, her blood pressure suddenly dropped and she appeared paralyzed. How could this happen?

   > Qtype:»Application Outline:»III.D.   Text pp.»416
   > Answers:»Whiplash injuries frequently cause spinal shock which is usually a transient period of functional loss following the injury. Symptoms include loss of all reflex activity caudal to the injury, bowel and bladder reflex loss, failing blood pressure and cessation of muscular activity.

3. Lucy is suffering from right sided paralysis and sensory loss. She cannot speak at all. Cerebral angiography and a CAT scan have shown no cerebral vascular defects, but the CAT scan did reveal a left-sided mass wedged between the diencephalon and the basal ganglia. Using your knowledge of anatomy, explain Lucy`s symptoms in terms of the specific lesion site.

   > Qtype:»Application Outline:»II.D.2.   Text pp.»383-386
   > Answers:»The mass, located on the left side, will affect the right side of the body due to brain lateralization. The mass is probably affecting the thalamus as well, which is the major sensory discriminatory structure. Finally, the location of this mass would also affect the primary motor cortex in the precentral gyrus, and specifically Broca's area, which is usually located in the left hemisphere.

4. On performing an autopsy on a 60-year old man, a medical student found the man had no corpus callosum. Apparently the man had functioned well neurologically because his medical history reported no neural dysfunctions. Explain why this finding does or does not surprise you.

   > Qtype:»Application Outline:»II.D.3.A.   Text pp.»389-391
   > Answers:»The corpus callosum is composed of commissural tracts which allow communication between the right and left hemispheres. Since one hemisphere is normally dominant, usually the left, there is no absolute requirement for communication. Projection fibers can interconnect the brain and cord and the brain pathways will adjust as necessary. If the anterior commissure is still present, it is possible that the necessary linkages could be made via this pathway.

13

The Peripheral Nervous System and Reflex Activity

CHAPTER PREVIEW

This chapter will focus on the cranial and spinal nerves of the peripheral nervous system that communicate with the brain and spinal cord of the central nervous system. It will then describe some of the important spinal reflexes, especially as they involve somatic function.

AT A GLANCE

INTEGRATING THE PACKAGE

SUGGESTED LECTURE OUTLINE

I. Overview of the Peripheral Nervous System (pp. 423-430)
    A. Sensory Receptors (pp. 424-426)
        1. Classification of Sensory Receptors
           a. According to Location
           b. According to the Stimulus Type Detected
           c. According to Structural Complexity
        2. Anatomy of the General Sensory Receptors

REVIEW ITEMS

---

11. Descending tracts of the spinal cord, (Chapter 12, p. 416)

12. Spinal roots, (Chapter 12, p. 409)

13. Gray and white mater of the spinal cord, (Chapter 12, pp. 409-411)

CROSS-REFERENCES

1. Cutaneous sensory receptors are presented in Chapter 5, p. 140-143.

2. Sensory receptors for the special senses and generator potentials are further described in detail in Chapter 16.

3. Spinal reflexes and the physiology of the sexual response is described in Chapter 28, p. 944.

4. Reflex activity and the control of digestive secretions is described in detail in Chapter 24, p. 789.

5. The nerve plexuses involved in digestion are mentioned in Chapter 24, p. 771.

6. The function of the vagus nerve in parasympathetic control is examined in Chapters 19, p. 626; 24, p. 788.

7. The cranial nerves associated with their special senses are covered in Chapter 16.

8. Relfex activity of the special senses is examined in Chapter 16.

9. Receptor and generator potentials as related to neural integration are described in Chapter 15, p. 477.

10. Spinal reflex control of micturition is examined in Chapter 26, p. 897-898)

ANSWERS TO TEXTBOOK CHAPTER QUESTIONS

Multiple Choice/Matching

1. b

2. c

3. c

4. (1)f; (2)i; (3)b; (4) g,h,l; (5)e; (6)i; (7)c; (8)k; (9)l; (10)c,d,f,k

5. (1)b 6; (2)d 1,8; (3)c 2; (4)c 5; (5)a 4; (6)a 3,9; (7) a 7; (8) a 7; (9)d 1

6. b, 1
   a, 3 and 5
   a, 4
   a, 2
   c, 2

7. b

Short Answer Essay Questions

8. The PNS enables the CNS to receive information and carry out its decisions. (p. 423)

9. The PNS includes all nervous tissue outside the CNS, that is, the sensory receptors, the peripheral nerves (cranial or spinal), the ganglia, and motor nerve endings. The peripheral nerves transmit sensory and motor impulses, the ganglia contain cell bodies of sensory or autonomic nerve fibers, the sensory receptors receive stimuli, and the motor end plates release neurotransmitters that regulate the activity of the effectors. (p. 423)

10. A receptor potential is like an EPSP in that it is a graded potential that changes membrane permeability and can help to generate an action potential. It differs from an EPSP in its stimulus, i.e., a type of energy (light pressure, etc.) versus a chemical neurotransmitter in the case of the EPSP. (pp. 425-427)

11. Schwann cells aid the regeneration process physically and chemically. Oligodendrocytes die and thus do not aid fiber regeneration. (pp. 428-430)

12. a. Spinal nerves form from dorsal and ventral roots that unite distal to the dorsal root ganglion. Spinal nerves are mixed. (See Fig. 13.5, p. 439)
    b. The ventral rami contribute large plexi that supply the anterior and lateral parts of the body, trunk, and the limbs. The dorsal rami supply the muscles and skin of the back (posterior trunk). (p. 439)

13. a. A plexus is a branching nerve network that ensures that any damage to one nerve root will not result in total loss of innervation to that part of the body. (p. 440)
    b. See Figs. 13.6 to 13.9, and Tables 13.3 to 13.6, pps. 440-445, for detailed information about each of the four plexuses.

14. Ipsilateral reflexes involve a reflex affecting the same side of the body (p. 451); contralateral reflexes involve a reflex that is initiated on one side of the body and affects the other side. (p. 452)

15. The flexor or withdrawal reflex is a protective mechanism to withdraw from a painful stimulus. (p. 452)

16. Flexor reflexes are protective ipsilateral, polysynaptic and prepotent reflexes, whereas crossed extensor reflexes consist of an ipsilateral withdrawal reflex and a contralateral extensor reflex that aids usually in balance. (pp. 442 and 443.)

17. Reflex tests assess the condition of the nervous system. Exaggerated, distorted, or absent reflexes indicate degeneration or pathology of specific regions of the nervous system before other signs are apparent. (p. 448)

18. Dermatomes are related to the sensory innervation regions of the spinal nerves. The spinal nerves correlate with the segmented body plan, as do the muscles (at least embryologically). (pp. 446-447)

Critical Thinking and Application Questions

1. Precise realignment of cut, regenerated axons with their former effector targets is highly unlikely. Coordination between nerve-muscle will have to be relearned. Additionally, not all fibers regenerate. (pp.428-430)

2. He would have problems dorsiflexing his right foot and his knee joint would be unstable (more rocking of the femur from side-to-side on the tibia). (p. 446)

3. Damage to the brachial plexus occurred when he suddenly stopped his descent (fall) by grabbing the branch. (p. 443)

4. The left trochlear nerve (IV) which innervates the superior oblique muscle responsible for this action. (p. 433)

LABORATORY CORRELATIONS

1. Marieb, E. N. <u>Human Anatomy and Physiology Laboratory Manual: Cat and Fetal Pig Versions</u>. 3rd. ed. Benjamin/Cummings, 1989.

    Exercise 22: Human Reflex Physiology

2. Marieb, E. N. <u>Human Anatomy and Physiology Laboratory Manual: Brief Version</u>. 3rd. ed. Benjamin/Cummings, 1992.

    Exercise 19: Human Reflex Physiology

OVERHEAD TRANSPARENCIES INDEX

Transparency	Description
13.1b	Structure of a nerve
13.3	Summary of location and function of the cranial nerves
13.4	Distribution of spinal nerves, posterior view
13.5	Formation and branches of spinal nerves
13.7a	Roots, trunks, divisions, and cords of the brachial plexus
13.11	Basic components of all human reflex arcs
13.12	Anatomy of the muscle spindle and Golgi tendon organ

BASSETT ATLAS SLIDES AND FIGURES INDEX

Slide #	Figure	Description
9	1.9A,B	Spinal cord, origin
10	1.10	Spinal cord, cauda equina
11	1.11A,B	Spinal cord, detail
12	2.1A,B	Parotid gland and facial nerve
19	3.3A,B	Chest wall removed

BLACK LINE MASTER INDEX

INSTRUCTIONAL AIDS

LECTURE HINTS

1. Emphasize again the distinction between central and peripheral nervous system, although stressing that the nervous system functions as a continuous unit even though we like to study its anatomy in bits and pieces. Students often treat each section as if it operates autonomously without regard to what may be happening in other parts of the nervous system.

2. Many students will still have a difficult time with the difference between receptor potentials, generator potentials, and action potentials. It is worth some time to be sure the distinction is clear.

3. As the anatomy of the nerve is discusses, point out the similarity between the basic structure of muscle tissue and nervous tissue. Also bring to students attention the similarity in nomenclature and point out that knowing the structure of muscle, they already know nerve anatomy (with slight changes in names.)

4. Students often have problems with neuron regeneration and myelination (i.e., CNS and PNS neurons are both myelinated) and why regeneration occurs in the PNS and not in the CNS. Spend time explaining the difference or refer the class to Chapter 11 to review myelination, the sheath of Schwann, and oligodendrocytes.

5. Try a diagram (cross-section) of the spinal cord indicating the dorsal and ventral roots and an extension into a short section of the spinal nerve. Draw arrows in these pathways indicating the direction of information flow. Remind the class that the brain must always receive information from an area in order to effect a change if necessary (the reason for two-way traffic in each level of the cord). In this way students are more likely to remember the anatomical relationship between these structures since they can logically relate material from a previous chapter to the material presented in this chapter.

6. Try asking specific questions of the class in order to promote student involvment. This technique holds student attention and more importantly, enforces the logical thought processes necessary in order to thoroughly comprehend physiological concepts. The reflex arc is an excellent tool to employ this strategy, since by this time the class has a general knowledge of all the components necessary to construct a generalized arc. After a brief introduction to the reflex arc and what its general function is, ask questions such as: " If we wanted to construct a reflex arc, what could we use to convert a stimulus to a nervous impulse?" Lead the class by a series of questions to the complete construction of the basic reflex arc, then go into the modifications of the basic blueprint to describe specific arc types and their functions. Students will not forget the reflex arc since they have constructed it themselves.

DEMONSTRATIONS/ACTIVITIES

1. Film(s) or other audiovisual materials of choice.

2. Select a student to help in the illustration of reflexes, such as patellar, plantar, abdominal, etc.

3. Obtain a skull to illustrate the locations, exit, and entrance of several cranial nerves, such as the olfactory, optic, and trigeminal.

4. Obtain a sheep brain with the cranial nerves intact to illustrate their locations.

5. Obtain a 3-D model of the peripheral nervous system to illustrate the distribution of the spinal nerves.

6. Obtain a 3-D model of a spinal cord cross section to illustrate the five components of a reflex arc and to illustrate terms such as ipsilateral, contralateral, monosynaptic, etc.

CRITICAL THINKING/DISCUSSION TOPICS

1. How can the injection of novocaine into one area of the lower jaw anesthetize one entire side of the jaw and tongue?

2. How can seat belts for both the front and back seat passengers of a car prevent serious neurological damage? How can using lap belts only cause severe damage?

3. Some over-eager parents swing their newborn infants around by the hands. What damage could this cause?

4. Pregnant women often experience numbness in their fingers and toes. Why?

5. Animals have considerably more reflexive actions than humans. Why?

LIBRARY RESEARCH TOPICS

1. How does acupuncture relate to the distribution of spinal nerves?

2. Will all victims of polio be rendered paralyzed? What different forms are there?

3. How has microsurgery been used to reconnect severed peripheral nerves?

4. What techniques can be employed to increase our reflexive actions?

AUDIO VISUAL AIDS/COMPUTER SOFTWARE

Films

1. The Peripheral Nervous System (IFB, 19 min., ., 1977) Demonstrates an infant's reflex action, the explains the components of the spinal reflex arc and the importance of conscious bodily control.

2. Spinal Nerves (UT, 18 min., C, 1976) The spinal nerves and their relationship to the sympathetic chain illustrated with the use of animation, photomicrography, and electron microscopic studies.

Filmstrips/Slides

1. The Reflex Arc (NTA, #70, Microviewer)

See *Guide to Audiovisual Resources* at the end of this module for key to AV distributors

---

LECTURE ENHANCEMENT MATERIAL

CLINICAL AND RELATED TERMS

1. Achilles Reflex - a reflex involving the plantar extension of the foot, following a tap on the Achilles tendon.

2. Anal reflex - a reflex involving the contraction of the anal sphincter or irritation of the anal skin.

3. Areflexia - absence of reflexes.

4. Carpal Tunnel Syndrome - a syndrome resulting from the compression of the median nerve in the carpal tunnel, resulting in pain, and burning and tingling of the fingers and hands.

5. Corneal Reflex - a reflex involving the closure of the eyelids due to irritation of the cornea.

6. Cremasteric Reflex - a reflex involving the contraction of the ipsilateral cremaster muscle that draws the testis upward following stroking of the inner aspect of the thigh.

7. Crutch Palsy - paralysis to the brachial plexus due to pressure to the axilla from prolonged use of a crutch.

8. Delayed Nerve Grafting - a surgical technique involving the removal of damaged sections of a spinal cord and the replacement of nerve segments from an arm or leg.

9. Gangliectomy - the surgical removal of a ganglion.

10. Nerve Block - regional anesthesia obtained by an injection of anesthetics in close proximity to the appropriate nerve.

11. Neurectomy - excision of a portion of a nerve.

12. Neurectopia - displacement of a nerve.

13. Neuroanastomosis - the surgical anastomosis of one nerve to another.

14. Neurolysis - surgical breaking up of perineural adhesions.

15. Neurorrhaphy - the suturing of a nerve.

16. Neurotomy - dissection of a nerve.

17. Phrenicotomy - excision or resection of the phrenic nerve.

18. Polyneuritis - inflammation of multiple nerves.

19. Radiculitis - inflammation of a spinal nerve root.

20. Radiculoneuritis (Guillain - Barre Syndrome) - a syndrome characterized by an absence of fever, pain, or tenderness of muscle, motor weakness, and absence of tendon reflexes. A type of encephalitis.

21. Rhizotomy - interruption of the nerve roots in the spinal canal.

22. Thoracic Outlet Syndrome - a compression of the brachial plexus resulting in pain to the arms, numbness of the fingers, and wasting of the muscles of the hand.

DISORDERS/HOMEOSTATIC IMBALANCES

Tumors of Peripheral Nerves

1. Acoustic Neuroma - a benign tumor within the auditory canal arising from the 8th cranial (acoustic) nerve.

2. Neuroblastoma - a sarcoma derived from nervous tissue, chiefly neuroblasts. Primarily affects young children, usually arising in the autonomic nervous system.

3. Neurofibroma - a benign tumor of peripheral nerves due to an abnormal proliferation of Schwann cells. Also known as a fibroneuroma.

4. Neurilemoma - a tumor of a peripheral nerve sheath (neurilemma). Also known as a Schwannoma.

5. Neurosarcoma - a sarcoma with neuromatous elements.

Infections and Inflammations

1. Guillain - Barre Syndrome - idiopathic polyneuritis. Characterized by a widespread patchy demyelination of spinal nerves and nerve roots, with some inflammatory changes. Symptoms include muscular weakness, beginning in the legs and spreading to the trunk. Recovery is slow.

2. Peripheral Neuritis (Polyneuritis) - an inflammation of spinal nerves, characterized by muscular weakness, numbness, and tingling, tenderness, and pain. Usually caused by systemic chronic disorder such as diabetes, alcoholism, etc.

3. Shingles - an acute viral infection, manifested along sensory root ganglia and caused by the herpes simplex virus. The disease exhibits vesicular eruptions along the area of distribution of the sensory nerve.

APPLIED PHARMACOLOGY

Local Anesthetics

1. Lidocaine (Xylocaine, Benzocaine, Nupercainal Creme) - used to relieve pain and itch of sunburn, insect bites, and hemorrhoids, and for peripheral, sympathetic, epidural, and spinal nerve blocks. Inhibits initiation and transmission of nerve impulses by lowering permeability of neural membrane to sodium ions.

2. Procaine (Novocaine) - similar to lidocaine, but requires a higher concentration for its affect and has a slower onset.

3. Tetracaine - similar to lidocaine, but requires a lower concentration for its affect, has a slower onset, but lasts longer.

Drugs for Lancinating Root Pain

1. Phenytoin (Dilantin) - used for Tic douloureux and to help prevent epileptic seizures. Acts by promoting sodium loss from nerve fibers, thus stabilizing membrane and inhibiting nerve impulse transmission.

SUGGESTED READINGS

1. Barr, M.L., and J.A. Kiernan. The Human Nervous System. 4th ed. New York:Harper & Row, 1983.

2. Cowan, R. "Antibodies Enhance Spinal Nerve Regrowth." Science News 137 (Jan. 20, 1990):38.

3. Easton, T.A. On the Normal Use of Reflexes. American Scientist 60 (Sept.-Oct. 1972).

4. Guyton, A.C. Basic Neuroscience: Anatomy and Physiology. Philadelphia: Saunders, 1987.

5. Mathers, L.H. "The Peripheral Nervous System." Stoneham, MA. Butterworth Pub., 1984.

6. Noback, C.T., and R. Demarest. The Human Nervous System. 3rd ed. New York:McGraw-Hill, 1980.

7. Schmidt, R.F. Fundamentals of Sensory Physiology. 3rd. ed. NewYork: Springer-Verlag. 1986.

8. Shepherd, G.M. Neurobiology. New York:Oxford Univ. Press., 1983.

9. Terry, G. "The Nervous System: Repairs to the Network." New Scientist 10 (Jun. 1989):1-4.

10. Weiss, R. "Neurons Regenerate Into Spinal Cord." Science News 132 (Nov. 21, 1987):324.

11. Weiss, R. "Regenerated Nerves Send First Messages." Science News 136 (Oct. 14, 1989):244.

12. Willis, W.D., and R.G. Grossman. Medical Neurobiology. 3rd ed. St. Louis:C.V. Mosby, 1981.

HANDOUTS

The following section contains prepared handout material which may be photocopied and distributed to the class. All materials are organized so that selected items can be cut and pasted for the instructors individual needs.

If budgets are a limiting factor in the use of handouts, these masters may be placed on reserve in the library for students to photocopy at their convenience.

Preview Of Selected Key Terms

Peripheral nervous system . . . . Portion of the nervous system consisting of nerves and ganglia that lie outside of the brain and spinal cord.

Somatic nervous system . . . . (soma=body) Division of the peripheral nervous system that provides the motor innervation of skeletal muscles.

Cranial nerves . . . . The 12 nerve pairs that arise from the brain.

Spinal nerves . . . . The 31 nerve pairs that arise from the spinal cord.

Plexus . . . . (plexus=braid) A network of converging and diverging nerve fibers.

Spinal reflex . . . . A somatic reflex mediated through the spinal cord.

Terms/Disorders

1. Achilles Reflex - a reflex involving the plantar extension of the foot, following a tap on the Achilles tendon.

2. Areflexia - absence of reflexes.

3. Carpal Tunnel Syndrome - a syndrome resulting from the compression of the median nerve in the carpal tunnel, resulting in pain, and burning and tingling of the fingers and hands.

4. Corneal Reflex - a reflex involving the closure of the eyelids due to irritation of the cornea.

5. Crutch Palsy - paralysis to the brachial plexus due to pressure to the axilla from prolonged use of a crutch.

6. Delayed Nerve Grafting - a surgical technique involving the removal of damaged sections of a spinal cord and the replacement of nerve segments from an arm or leg.

7. Lidocaine (Xylocaine, Benzocaine, Nupercainal Creme) - used to relieve pain and itch of sunburn, insect bites, and hemorrhoids, and for peripheral, sympathetic, epidural, and spinal nerve blocks. Inhibits initiation and transmission of nerve impulses by lowering permeability of neural membrane to sodium ions.

8. Nerve Block - regional anesthesia obtained by an injection of anesthetics in close proximity to the appropriate nerve.

9. Neuroblastoma - a sarcoma derived from nervous tissue, chiefly neuroblasts. Primarily affects young children, usually arising in the autonomic nervous system.

10. Neurofibroma - a benign tumor of peripheral nerves due to an abnormal proliferation of Schwann cells. Also known as a fibroneuroma.

11. Neurilemoma - a tumor of a peripheral nerve sheath (neurilemma). Also known as a Schwannoma.

12. Neurosarcoma - a sarcoma with neuromatous elements.

13. Peripheral Neuritis (Polyneuritis) - an inflammation of spinal nerves, characterized by muscular weakness, numbness, and tingling, tenderness, and pain. Usually caused by systemic chronic disorder such as diabetes, alcoholism, etc.

14. Phenytoin (Dilantin) - used for Tic douloureux and to help prevent epileptic seizures. Acts by promoting sodium loss from nerve fibers, thus stabilizing membrane and inhibiting nerve impulse transmission.

15. Polyneuritis - inflammation of multiple nerves.

16. Procaine (Novocaine) - similar to lidocaine, but requires a higher concentration for its affect and has a slower onset.

17. Radiculoneuritis (Guillain - Barre Syndrome) - a syndrome characterized by an absence of fever, pain, or tenderness of muscle, motor weakness, and absence of tendon reflexes. A type of encephalitis.

18. Shingles - an acute viral infection, manifested along sensory root ganglia and caused by the herpes simplex virus. The disease exhibits vesicular eruptions along the area of distribution of the sensory nerve.

Age Associated Changes

General Age Related Changes

- Reflexes slow
- Receptor atrophy
- Decrease in muscle tone
  - Probably due to loss of CNS neurons
  - Increased sluggishness of CNS processing circuits
- Peripheral nerves thenselves remain viable throughout life unless traumatized.
- Reduced cardiac delivery to peripheral nervous tissue results in ischemic conditions.
- Ischemia results in numbness in the affected area.

The following section contains selected unlabeled line art representations of key elements in this chapter. These diagrams may be utilized in several ways depending on individual needs:

1. Photocopy directly onto acetate film for overhead projection during class lecture/discussion. The art is unlabeled so that the instructor may write directly on the acetate during class and emphasize critical features. A key advantage in the use of this form of visual presentation is the ease with which students are able to comprehend complex anatomical and physiological relationships presented during class.

2. Photocopy for handouts so that the students may take notes directly on the diagrams and in that way have a clear understanding of the relationship between the figure and lecture material.

3. If the course is on a tight budget, place masters of diagrams on reserve (usually in a notebook in the library) for students to make copies should they choose to do so.

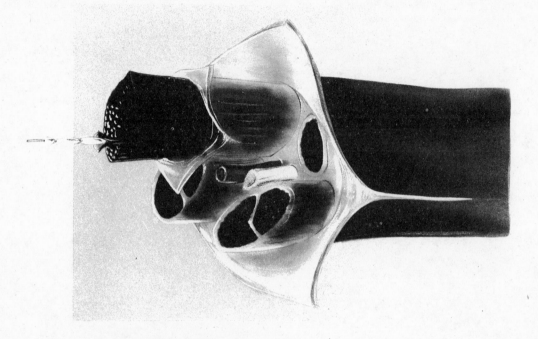

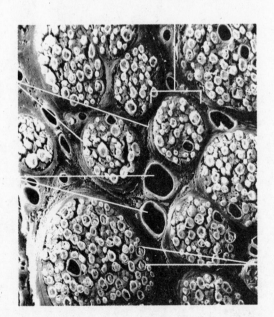

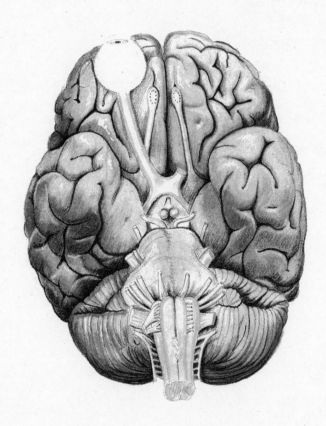

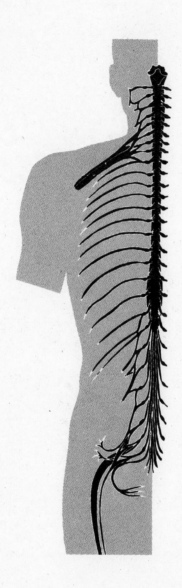

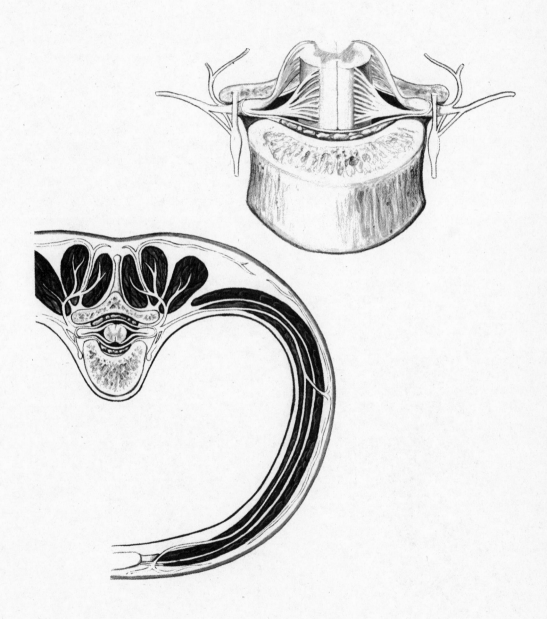

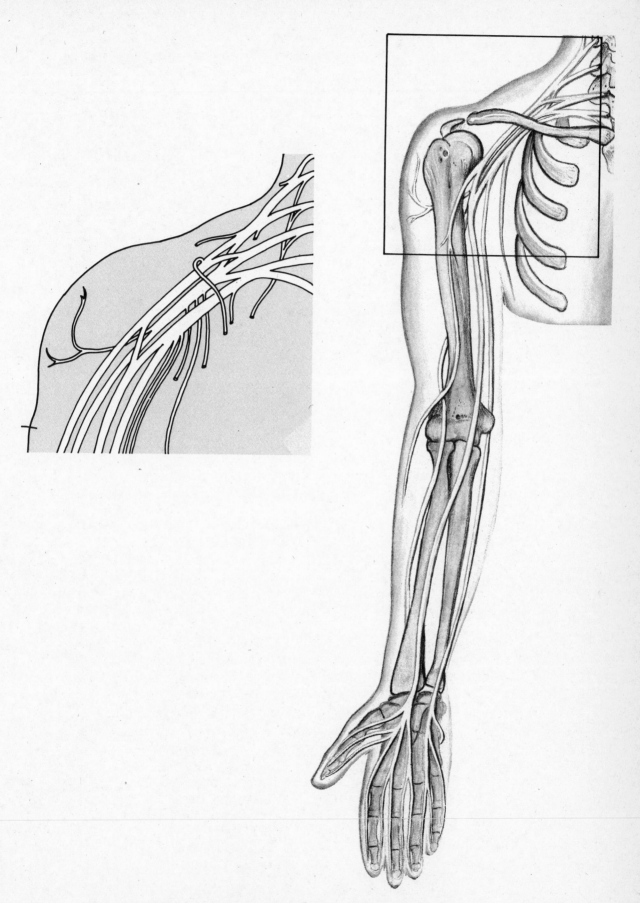

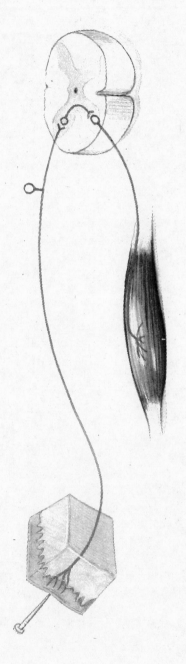

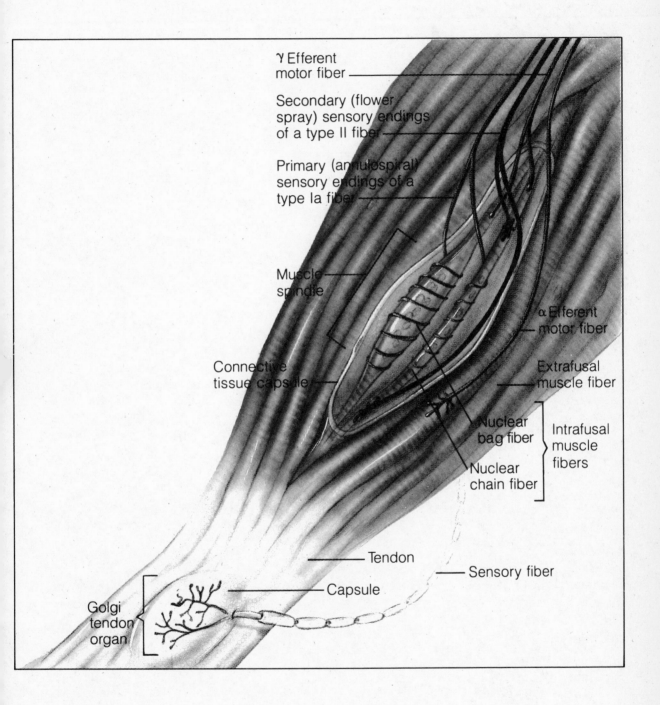

γ Efferent
motor fiber

Secondary (flower
spray) sensory endings
of a type II fiber

Primary (annulospiral)
sensory endings of a
type Ia fiber

Muscle
spindle

α Efferent
motor fiber

Connective
tissue capsule

Extrafusal
muscle fiber

Nuclear
bag fiber

Intrafusal
muscle
fibers

Nuclear
chain fiber

Tendon

Sensory fiber

Capsule

Golgi
tendon
organ

MATCHING QUESTIONS

Match the following:

a. Abducens
b. Accessory
c. Facial
d. Glossopharyngeal
e. Hypoglossal
f. Oculomotor

g. Olfactory
h. Optic
i. Trigeminal
j. Trochlear
k. Vagus
l. Vestibulocochlear

___ 1. Causes lens shape changes during visual accommodation.
___ 2. Is the chief motor nerve of the face.
___ 3. Serves the tongue muscles.
___ 4. Consists of three major divisions.
___ 5. Allows you to smile.
___ 6. Is impaired in Bell's palsy.
___ 7. Helps to regulate blood pressure and digestion.
___ 8. Serves the senses of audition and equilibrium.
___ 9. Forms a cross pattern called a chiasma.
___10. Formed by the union of a cranial and a spinal root.

Qtype:»Memory   Outline:»II.   Text pp.»430-438
Answers:»1-f; 2-c; 3-d,e; 4-i; 5-c; 6-c; 7-k; 8-l; 9-h; 10-b

Match the reflex with the appropriate description

a. abdominal
b. crossed extensor
c. flexor

d. stretch
d. deep tendon
f. plantar

___ 1. Produces a rapid withdrawal of the body part from a painful stimulus; ipsilateral.
___ 2. Tests both upper and lower motor pathways. The sole of the foot is stimulated with a dull instrument extension.
___ 3. Provides for both ipsilateral withdrawal and contralateral extension.
___ 4. Prevents muscle overstretching and maintains muscle tone.
___ 5. Checks the integrity of the spinal cord and dorsal rami at the level of T-8 to T-12.

Qtype:»Memory   Outline:»IV.B.   Text pp.»447-453
Answers:»1-c; 2-f; 3-b; 4-d; 5-a

Match the following:

a. Cervical plexus
b. Brachial plexus
c. Lumbar plexus

d. Sacral plexus
e. Coeliac plexus

___ 1. Trauma to a nerve of this plexus may cause wristdrop.
___ 2. Improper administration of an injection to the buttocks may injure a nerve of this plexus.
___ 3. Obturator and femoral nerves are from this plexus.
___ 4. Phrenic nerve is formed from this plexus.
___ 5. Striking the funny bone may cause injury to a nerve of this plexus.
___ 6. Largest and longest nerve of the body is in this plexus.

___ 7. Irritation of a major nerve of this plexus may cause hiccups.

Qtype:»Memory   Outline:»III.C.   Text pp.»440-446
Answers:»1-b; 2-d; 3-c; 4-a; 5-b; 6-d; 7-a

TRUE/FALSE QUESTIONS

1. Another word for root is rami.
                a. true   b. false

Qtype:»Memory   Outline:»III.B.2.   Text pp.»439
Answers:»false

2. The meningeal branch actually reenters the vertebral canal to innervate the meninges, vertebrae, and ligaments.
                a. true   b. false

Qtype:»Memory   Outline:»III.B.2.c.   Text pp.»439
Answers:»true

3. The cervical plexus is buried deep under the sternocleidomastoid muscle.
                a. true   b. false

Qtype:»Memory   Outline:»III.C.1.a.   Text pp.»440
Answers:»true

4. The obturator nerve is formed by the lumbar plexus.
                a. true   b. false

Qtype:»Memory   Outline:»III.C.3.a.   Text pp.»444
Answers:»true

5. Reciprocal inhibition means that while one sensory nerve is stimulated another sensory neuron in the same area is inhibited and cannot respond.
                a. true   b. false

Qtype:»Concept   Outline:»IV.B.2.a.   Text pp.»449
Answers:»false

6. There are 37 pairs of spinal nerves.
                a. true   b. false

Qtype:»Memory   Outline:»III.A.   Text pp.»438
Answers:»false

7. The glossopharyngeal is the only cranial nerve that contains sensory fibers.
                        a. true   b. false

Qtype:»Memory   Outline:»II.I.   Text pp.»436
Answers:»false

---

8. If the dorsal root of a spinal nerve were cut, the result in the tissue or region would be a complete loss of sensation.
                        a. true   b. false

Qtype:»Concept   Outline:»III.B.1.a.   Text pp.»439
Answers:»true

---

9. A major nerve of the brachial plexus would be the obturator.
                        a. true   b. false

Qtype:»Memory   Outline:»III.C.2.   Text pp.»441
Answers:»false

---

10. A cranial nerve that forms a chiasma at the base of the brain for partial crossover of neural fibers would be the oculomotor nerve.
                        a. true   b. false

Qtype:»Memory   Outline:»II.B.2.   Text pp.»433
Answers:»false

---

11. External strabismus and ptosis could be caused by damage to the oculomotor nerve.
                        a. true   b. false

Qtype:»Application Outline:»II.C.3.   Text pp.»433
Answers:»true

---

12. The trigeminal nerve has three branches which innervate portions of the maxillary, mandibular, and ophthalmic areas.
                        a. true   b. false

Qtype:»Memory   Outline:»II.E.1.   Text pp.»434
Answers:»true

---

13. Tic douloureux is a painful condition occurring with the facial nerve.
                        a. true   b. false

Qtype:»Application Outline:»II.E.4.   Text pp.»434
Answers:»false

---

14. The only cranial nerve to extend beyond the head and neck region is the vagus nerve.
          a. true   b. false

Qtype:»Memory   Outline:»II.J.2.   Text pp.»437
Answers:»true

---

15. Cranial nerve XI is the abducens nerve.
          a. true   b. false

Qtype:»Memory   Outline:»II.K.   Text pp.»437
Answers:»false

---

16. If the vagus nerve were severed, the effect would probably be fatal.
          a. true   b. false

Qtype:»Concept   Outline:»II.J.3.   Text pp.»437
Answers:»true

---

17. Although spinal nerves are paired, most cranial nerves are not.
          a. true   b. false

Qtype:»Concept   Outline:»II.   Text pp.»430
Answers:»false

---

18. If the hypoglossal nerve was damaged, speech and swallowing would be impaired.
          a. true   b. false

Qtype:»Concept   Outline:»II.L.   Text pp.»438
Answers:»true

---

19. The dorsal ramus consists only of sensory nerves bringing information to the spinal cord.
          a. true   b. false

Qtype:»Memory   Outline:»III.B.2.a.   Text pp.»439
Answers:»false

---

20. Dermatomes are skin segments that relate to sensory innervation regions of the spinal nerves.
          a. true   b. false

Qtype:»Memory   Outline:»III.D.   Text pp.»446
Answers:»true

MULTIPLE-CHOICE QUESTIONS

1. A simple spinal reflex goes along which of the following reflex arcs?
    a. effector, afferent neuron, integration center, efferent neuron, receptor
    b. receptor, afferent neuron, integration center, efferent neuron, effector
    c. effector, efferent neuron, integration center, afferent neuron, receptor
    d. receptor, efferent neuron, integration center, afferent neuron, effector

    Qtype:»Memory   Outline:»IV.A.   Text pp.»448
    Answers:»b

2. Mixed cranial nerves containing both motor and sensory fibers include all but which of the following?
    a. oculomotor   d. facial
    b. vestibulocochlear   e. vagus
    c. trigeminal

    Qtype:»Memory   Outline:»II.   Text pp.»430-438
    Answers:»b

3. The "knee jerk" is an example of a:
    a. axon reflex.   d. cross extensor reflex.
    b. extensor thrust reflex.   e. stretch reflex.
    c. stress reflex.

    Qtype:»Memory   Outline:»IV.B.2.   Text pp.»451
    Answers:»e

4. The flexor muscles in the anterior arm (biceps brachii and brachialis) are innervated by what nerve?
    a. radial   c. ulnar
    b. median   d. musculocutaneous

    Qtype:»Memory   Outline:»III.C.2.c.   Text pp.»441
    Answers:»d

5. The cranial nerves that have neural connections with the tongue include all but the:
    a. trigeminal.   d. trochlear.
    b. facial.   e. hypoglossal.
    c. glossopharyngeal.

    Qtype:»Memory   Outline:»II.D.   Text pp.»433
    Answers:»d

6. Nerves to the skeletal muscle are derived from the:
   a. somatic division of the nervous system.
   b. autonomic nervous system.
   c. sympathetic division of the ANS.
   d. afferent division of the ANS.
   e. All of the above are correct.

   Qtype:»Memory   Outline:»I.   Text pp.»423
   Answers:»a

_____

7. A patient who received a blow to the side of the skull (parotid area) exhibits the following signs and symptoms on that side of the face: he is unable to close his eye and the corner of his mouth droops. Which cranial nerve has been damaged?
   a. facial   c. hypoglossal
   b. glossopharyngeal   d. accessory

   Qtype:»Application Outline:»II.G.   Text pp.»435
   Answers:»a

_____

8. Which of the following nerves does **not** arise from the brachial plexus?
   a. median   c. radial
   b. phrenic   d. ulnar

   Qtype:»Memory   Outline:»III.C.2.   Text pp.»443
   Answers:»b

_____

9. If the ventral root of a spinal nerve were cut, what would be the result in the tissue or region that nerve supplies?
   a. complete loss of sensation
   b. a complete loss of voluntary movement
   c. loss of neither sensation nor movement but only of autonomic control
   d. a complete loss of sensation and movement

   Qtype:»Concept   Outline:»III.B.1.b.   Text pp.»438
   Answers:»b

_____

10. The posterior side of the thigh, leg, and foot is served by the _____ nerve.
    a. obturator   c. tibial
    b. peroneal   d. femoral

    Qtype:»Memory   Outline:»III.C.3.b.   Text pp.»445
    Answers:»c

_____

11. Problems in balance may follow trauma to which nerve?
    a. abducens
    b. vestibulocochlear
    c. trigeminal
    d. accessory

    Qtype:»Concept   Outline:»II.H.   Text pp.»436
    Answers:»b

---

12. Which of the following regions is **not** innervated by nerves of the sacral plexus?
    a. gluteus maximus
    b. abdominal wall
    c. foot
    d. external genitalia
    e. perineum

    Qtype:»Memory   Outline:»III.C.3.b.   Text pp.»446
    Answers:»b

---

13. Starting, in order, at the spinal cord, the subdivisions of the brachial plexus are:
    a. rami, trunks, divisions, and cords.
    b. rami, divisions, cords, and trunks.
    c. divisions, rami, trunks, and cords.
    d. trunks, divisions, cords, and rami.

    Qtype:»Memory   Outline:»III.C.2.a.   Text pp.»442
    Answers:»a

---

14. The cranial nerve with a dual origin (brain and spinal cord) is the:
    a. hypoglossal.
    b. accessory.
    c. vagus.
    d. glossopharyngeal.

    Qtype:»Memory   Outline:»II.K.   Text pp.»437
    Answers:»b

---

15. Which of the following is **not** a nerve plexus?
    a. brachial
    b. cervical
    c. lumbar
    d. sacral
    e. thoracic

    Qtype:»Memory   Outline:»III.C.   Text pp.»440-446
    Answers:»e

---

16. A major nerve of the cervical plexus is the:
    a. phrenic.
    b. vagus.
    c. sciatic.
    d. radial.

    Qtype:»Memory   Outline:»III.C.1.b.   Text pp.»441
    Answers:»a

---

17. Spinal nerves exiting the cord from the level of L-4 to S-4 form the:
    a. lumbar plexus.
    b. femoral plexus.
    c. sacral plexus.
    d. thoracic plexus.

    Qtype:»Memory   Outline:»III.C.3.b.   Text pp.»446
    Answers:»c

18. A fracture of the ethmoid bone would result in damage to which cranial nerve?
    a. glossopharyngeal
    b. vagus
    c. olfactory
    d. accessory

    Qtype:»Concept   Outline:»II.A.   Text pp.»432
    Answers:»c

19. The abducens nerve:
    a. supplies innervation to lateral rectus muscles of the eye.
    b. relays sensory information from taste buds on the tongue.
    c. exits from the medulla.
    d. if paralyzed, exhibits Bell's palsy.

    Qtype:»Concept   Outline:»II.F.3.   Text pp.»435
    Answers:»a

20. The neural branch that forms the plexi of the body is the:
    a. ramus communicates.
    b. meningeal branch.
    c. dorsal ramus.
    d. ventral ramus.

    Qtype:»Memory   Outline:»III.B.2.a.   Text pp.»440
    Answers:»d

20. A basic reflex:
    a. is a rapid, predictable, learned response.
    b. can be modified by learned behavior.
    c. are autonomic only.
    d. arc always has at least five elements.
    e. are always mediated by the brain.

    Qtype:»Memory   Outline:»IV.   Text pp.»447
    Answers:»b

21. Spinal reflexes:
   1. work even if the brain is destroyed.
   2. do not send information to the brain.
   3. function only in proprioception.
   a. 1 only
   b. 2 only
   c. 3 only
   d. 1 and 3
   e. 2 and 3

   Qtype:»Concept   Outline:»IV.B.   Text pp.»448
   Answers:»a

22. Striking the "funny bone" is actually stimulation of the:
   a. radial nerve.
   b. sciatic nerve.
   c. ulnar nerve.
   d. median nerve.
   e. axillary nerve.

   Qtype:»Concept   Outline:»III.C.2.e.   Text pp.»443
   Answers:»c

23. Select the statement that is most correct:
   a. Ganglia are collections of neuron cell bodies in the CNS that are associated with efferent fibers.
   b. Efferent ganglia can be associated with the autonomic system.
   c. The dorsal root ganglion is a motor only structure.
   d. Efferent ganglia are anatomically and functionally very simple.
   e. The cell bodies of afferent ganglia are located in the spinal cord.

   Qtype:»Concept   Outline:»III.B.   Text pp.»438
   Answers:»b

24. An improperly delivered gluteal injection could result in:
   a. neurofibromatosis
   b. postpoliomyelitis muscular atrophy
   c. shingles
   d. paresthesia
   e. sciatica

   Qtype:»Memory   Outline:»III.C.3.b.   Text pp.»446
   Answers:»e

25. Which of the following numbers of spinal nerves is correct?
   a. six cervical
   b. twelve thoracic
   c. six lumbar
   d. eight sacral
   e. eitht coccygeal

   Qtype:»Memory   Outline:»III.A.   Text pp.»438
   Answers:»b

26. Select the statement about plexuses that is most correct:
    a. The dorsal rami of all spinal nerves unite to form complex networks.
    b. Only ventral rami form plexuses.
    c. Each branch of the plexus contains fibers from a single spinal nerve.
    d. Any effector receives innervation from a single branch of a plexus.
    e. The ventral rami of thoracic spinal nerves unite to form the thoracic plexus.

        Qtype:»Memory   Outline:»III.C.   Text pp.»440
        Answers:»b

27. A reflex that causes muscle relaxation and lengthening in response to muscle contraction is called a:
    a. deep tendon reflex.
    b. patellar reflex.
    c. flexor reflex
    d. crossed extensor reflex.
    e. plantar reflex.

        Qtype:»Memory   Outline:»IV.B.2.   Text pp.»451
        Answers:»a

28. Protective reflexes are often prepotent which means:
    a. they inform the brain of existing conditions before action is taken.
    b. that the relfex is completed without conscious recognition.
    c. they override spinal pathways and prevent other reflexes from using them at the same time.
    d. they are pre-loaded for quick response.
    e. None of the above is correct.

        Qtype:»Memory   Outline:»IV.B.3.   Text pp.»452
        Answers:»c

29. During old age:
    1. sensory receptors atrophy.
    2. reaction time slowing is due primarily to peripheral nerve degeneration.
    3. reflexes occur more slowly.
    a. 1 only   d. 1 and 3
    b. 2 only   e. 2 and 3
    c. 3 only

        Qtype:»Concept   Outline:»V.   Text pp.»453
        Answers:»d

SHORT-ANSWER QUESTIONS

1. Define golgi tendon organs and muscle spindles relative to the stretch reflex.

   Qtype:»Concept   Outline:»IV.B.2.   Text pp.»448-449
   Answers:»Golgi tendon organs work with muscle spindles to act a proprioceptors in skeletal muscles and their associated tendons. When muscles are stretched due to contraction of antagonist muscles, the sensory neurons send inpulses to the spinal cord, where they synapse with motor neurons of the stretched muscle. Impulses are then sent to the stretched muscle which then resists further stretching. This prevents muscle tissue damage.

2. Distinguish between monosynaptic and polysynaptic reflexes and between ipsilateral and contralateral reflex responses.

   Qtype:»Memory   Outline:»IV.B.1.   Text pp.»448
   Answers:»Monosynaptic refers to a single synapse in the reflex arc (one sensory and one motor neuron). Polysynaptic refers to more than one synapse on the arc; involving sensory neurons, interneurons, and motor neurons. Ipsilateral refers to a reflex arc limited to one side of the spinal cord while contralateral reflexes cross to the opposite side.

3. What is the normal response of the plantar reflex? What is Babinski's sign and what does it indicate?

   Qtype:»Concept   Outline:»IV.B.5.a.   Text pp.»453
   Answers:»The plantar reflex tests the integrity of the spinal cord from L-4 to S-2 and also determines if corticospinal tracts are functioning and properly myelinated. The normal plantar response is downward flexion of the toes. If there is damage, the great toe dorsiflexes and smaller toes fan laterally (Babinski's sign). Infants, who normally lack complete myelination exhibit this sign.

4. List and describe the function of the three cranial nerves that service the eye (other than photoreception for vision).

   Qtype:»Memory   Outline:»II.   Text pp.»430-438
   Answers:»The three cranial nerves are: oculomotor, trochlear, and abducens. The oculomotor is mostly motor with branches to the inferior oblique and superior, inferior, the medial rectus muscles, and to the muscles of the iris and lens. The trochlear supplies mostly motor fibers to the superior oblique muscles of the eye. The abducens supplies mostly motor fibers to the lateral rectus muscle of the eye.

CLINICAL QUESTIONS

1. While working in the emergency room you receive two patients who were in an automobile accident. One is dead on arrival having suffered a transaction of the spinal cord at the level of C-2. The other patient suffered a similar injury but at the level of C-6 and is still alive. Explain briefly in terms of phrenic nerve origin and function, why one injury was fatal while the other was not.

   > Qtype:»Application Outline:»III.C.1.b.   Text pp.»440
   > Answers:»The phrenic nerve receives fibers from C-3 to C-5 and conveys inpulses to the
   > diaphragm. Damage to this nerve would cause respiratory arrest and death. The first
   > patient died because damage was above C-3 making the nerve non-functional. The
   > second person will be paralyzed from the neck down.

2. Ralph sustained a leg injury in a bowling accident and had to use crutches. Unfortunately, he never took the time to learn how to use them properly. After two weeks of use he noticed his fingers were becoming numb. Shortly, his arms were getting weaker and tingling. What could be his problem?

   > Qtype:»Application Outline:»III.C.2.f.   Text pp.»443
   > Answers:»Compression of the radial nerve (in the region of the armpit) may cause
   > temporary cessation of nervous transmission often called Saturday night paralysis.
   > Continued pressure could cause permanent damage.

3. George, a 20-year old man, injured his jaw and lost several teeth in a barroom brawl. Several weeks later he began to experience sharp stabbing pain in his lower jaw. After visiting the dentist he was told that he had trigeminal neuralgia. What is this condition and how is it treated?

   > Qtype:»Application Outline:»II.E.4.   Text pp.»434
   > Answers:»Trigeminal neuralgia or tic doulereaux is an inflammation of the trigeminal nerve
   > probably caused by the fight, and subsequent damage to the jaw.

4. David, an aspiring baseball player, was struck on the left side of his face with a fast ball pitch. He was not wearing a safety helmet. His zygomatic arch was crushed as well as parts of the temporal bone. Following the accident and reconstructive surgery, he noted his left lower eyelid was still drooping and the corner of his mouth sagged. What nerve damage did he sustain?

   > Qtype:»Application Outline:»II.G.3.   Text pp.»435
   > Answers:»He suffered facial nerve damage on his left side. Due to the bone damage,
   > branches to the eye and jaw were probably damaged. It is possible that the damage could
   > be reversible if the nerves were not cut or crushed completely.

The Autonomic Nervous System

14

CHAPTER PREVIEW

This chapter describes the complex internal regulating system, the autonomic nervous system. The anatomy and physiology of its two divisions, parasympathetic and sympathetic, will be illustrated in detail. How the two divisions interact to control most of our visceral organs and how they regulate homeostasis will then be presented.

AT A GLANCE

INTEGRATING THE PACKAGE

SUGGESTED LECTURE OUTLINE

I. Introduction (p. 457)

II. Overview of the Autonomic Nervous System (pp. 458-459)
    A. Comparison of the Somatic and Autonomic Nervous System (pp. 458-459)
        1. Effectors
        2. Efferent Pathways and Ganglia

REVIEW ITEMS

---

1. Membrane functions, (Chapter 3, pp. 66-76)

2. Membrane receptors, (Chapter 3, p. 74)

3. Nervous tissue, (Chapter 4, pp. 129-130)

4. Membrane potentials, (Chapter 11, p. 351)

5. Neuronal integration, (Chapter 11, pp. 370-373)

6. Serial and parallel processing, (Chapter 11, p. 372)

7. Synapses, (Chapter 11, p. 360)

8. Neurotransmitters, (Chapter 11, pp. 365-368)

9. Ascending tracts of ths spinal cord, (Chapter 12, p. 412)

10. Descending tracts of the spinal cord, (Chapter 12, p. 416)

11. Spinal roots, (Chapter 12, p. 409)

12. Gray and white mater of the spinal cord, (Chapter 12, pp. 409-411)

CROSS-REFERENCES

1. The role of the sympathetic and parasympathetic pathways (and epinephrine, norepinephrine) in medullary control of cardiac rate is explained in Chapter 19, p. 626.

2. Sympathetic and parasympathetic effects in human sexual response is detailed in Chapter 28, p. 944.

3. Sympathetic control of blood vessels to the kidney is described in Chapter 26, p. 876, 884.

4. Parasympathetic pelvic splanchnic nerves and the urinary system are further described in Chapter 26, p. 897-898.

5. Sympathetic and parasympathetic control of digestive processes is explained in Chapter 24.

6. Sympathetic control (and the effects of epinephrine and norepinephrine) of blood vessel diameter is further examined in Chapter 20, p. 642.

7. The fight/flight response is mentioned in Chapter 20, p. 644.

ANSWERS TO TEXTBOOK CHAPTER QUESTIONS

Multiple Choice/Matching

1. d

2. (1)S; (2)P; (3)P; (4)S; (5)S; (6)P; (7)P; (8)S; (9)P; (10)S; (11)P; (12)S

Short Answer Essay Questions

3. Involuntary nervous system is used to reflect its subconscious control; emotional-visceral system reflects the fact that the hypothalamus is the major regulatory center for both the emotional (limbic) response and visceral controls. The term visceral also indicates the location of most of its effectors. (p. 457)

4. White rami contain myelinated and preganglionic fibers that leave the spinal nerve to enter the paravertebral ganglion; gray rami represent axons of postganglionic neurons, are unmyelinated, and enter the spinal nerve. (p. 463, 465)

5. Sweat glands - increase the production of sweat; eye - pupils enlarge; adrenal medulla - releases norepinephrine and epinephrine; heart - increase in rate and force of contraction; lungs - bronchodilation; liver - glycogenolysis and the release of glucose to the blood; blood vessels to the skeletal muscles - dilation; blood vessels to digestive viscera - vonstriction; salivary glands - constriction of blood vessels supplying the gland causing a decrease in saliva production. (p. 469)

6. All except the effects on the adrenal medulla, liver, and blood vessels. (p. 469)

7. All preganglionic fibers and postganglionic fibers of the parasympathetic division secrete acetylcholine. Some postganglionic sympathetic fibers secrete acetylcholine. Only postganglionic fibers of sympathetic division release norepinephrine. (p. 467)

8. Sympathetic tone means that the vascular system is under a partial state of contraction. Parasympathetic tone maintains the tone of the digestive organs and keeps heart rate at the lowest level that maintains homeostasis. (pp. 468-469)

9. Acetylcholine - nicotinic and muscarinic; Norepinephrine - α_1, α_2, β_1, β_2. (pp. 467-468)

10. Reticular formation nuclei in the brain stem particularly in the medulla. (p. 471)

11. The hypothalamus is the main integration center that coordinates heart rate, blood pressure, body temperature, etc. (p. 472)

12. The premise of biofeedback training is that we do not routinely exert voluntary controls over our visceral activities because we have little conscious awareness of our internal environment. The training allows subjects to become aware of the signals and subsequently make subtle internal changes to help them control such things as migraine headaches, stress, etc. (p. 472)

13. Elderly people often complain of constipation and dry eyes, and faintness when position changes i.e., standing up abruptly after sitting. (p. 472)

Critical Thinking and Application Questions

1. Parasympathetic stimulation of the bladder via the release of acetylcholine increases bladder tone and releases the urinary sphincters, a result which will be reproduced by bethanechol. He will probably experience dizziness due to low blood pressure (decreased heart rate), deficient tear formation, wheezing, diarrhea, cramping, and undesirable erection of the penis - all parasympathetic effects. (p. 467-469)

2. Referred pain is the sensation of pain that appears to originate from a site other than that of the painful stimulus. Damage to the heart gives rise to pain impulses that enter the spinal cord in the thoracic region that also receives impulses from the left chest and arm. (p. 466)

3. Raynaud's disease. Smoking causes vasoconstriction i.e., the nicotine mimics the affects of acetylcholine on sympathetic nicotinic receptors of the skin blood vessels. (p. 472)

4. Hirschsprung's disease (congenital megacolon); the parasympathetic plexus supplying the distal part of the large intestine fails to develop normally, thus allowing feces to accumulate in the bowel. (p. 473)

LABORATORY CORRELATIONS

1. Marieb, E. N. <u>Human Anatomy and Physiology Laboratory Manual: Cat and Fetal Pig Versions</u>. 3rd. ed. Benjamin/Cummings, 1989.

   Exercise 19: Spinal Cord, Spinal Nerves, and Autonomic Nervous System

2. Marieb, E. N. <u>Human Anatomy and Physiology Laboratory Manual: Brief Version</u>. 3rd. ed. Benjamin/Cummings, 1992.

   Exercise 18: Spinal Cord, Spinal Nerves, and Autonomic Nervous System

OVERHEAD TRANSPARENCIES INDEX

Transparency	Description
14.1	Somatic/Autonomic nervous systems
14.2	Autonomic nervous system
14.4	Sympathetic pathways

BASSETT ATLAS SLIDES AND FIGURES INDEX

Slide #	Figure	Description
18	3.2	Anterior mediastinum
19	3.3A,B	Chest wall removed
22	3.6A,B	Lateral view of mediastinum

BLACK LINE MASTER INDEX

No Black Line Masters for Chapter 14.

INSTRUCTIONAL AIDS

LECTURE HINTS

1. Since the autonomic nervous system is more complex that the somatic nervous sytem, it it worthwhile to spend some time comparing and contrasting the anatomy of each.

2. Figure 14.4 is a good 3-D representation of sympathetic pathways, however as an initial introduction during lecture it is of benefit for the instructor to draw a 2-D schematic diagram of sympathetic and parasympathetic pathways so that the class can follow the construction of the circuit logically and understand how it is "wired," Then refer students to the overall construction presented in Figure 14.4, p. 464.

3. Emphasize that somatic efferent pathways consist of a motor neuron cell body in the CNS whose axon extends out through the PNS to directly innervate the skeletal muscle effector. In contrast, autonomic efferent pathways follow the sam general plan, but consist of two motor neurons in series.

4. Point out that in many cases sympathetic and parasympathetic synapses use different neurotransmitters, an essential characteristic in the dual nature of autonomic function. This will be illustrated when discussing fight/flight and rest/digest responses.

5. Many students have difficulty with the idea of neurotransmitter/receptor function. Point out that many substances similar in chemical constructing to the actual neurotransmitter are capable of generating the same response. Emphasize that it is the binding of a substance to a receptor that generates the cellular response.

6. To illustrate sympathetic tone, use the example of vasomotor control. Point out that dilation (to decrease blood pressure) is not a muscle contraction response, but that relaxation of the smooth muscle in the wall of the blood vessel is the actual cause. To vasoconstrict, increase sympathetic stimulation. Therefore in order for dilation to be possible, there must be a certain amount of constant sympathetic stimulation (tone) even during a relaxed state.

7. Emphasize that there is a constant level of parasympathetic stimulation (tone) to many visceral organs and that there is just enough sympathetic stimulation to keep systems in homeostasis. To probe the class for understanding, ask "What would happen to resting heart rate if parasympathetic stimulation were cut?"

DEMONSTRATIONS/ACTIVITIES

1. Film(s) or other audiovisual materials of choice.

2. Set up a live, exposed frog or turtle heart demonstration to illustrate the effects of acetylcholine and epinephrine.

3. Without announcing what you will be doing, walk quietly into the lecture room, set your notes down, and yell very loudly (to startle the students). Then, have each student prepare a list of all those organs that were affected and what the effect was.

4. Obtain a preserved cat and dissect it to illustrate the sympathetic nerve trunk, coeliac ganglia, splancnic nerves, and other portions of the ANS.

5. Obtain a 3-D model of a spinal cord cross section and longitudinal section that illustrates the parts of the ANS and especially the sympathetic and gray and white rami.

6. Use diagrams followed by Bassett Atlas slides to emphasize the anatomy of the autonomic pathways.

CRITICAL THINKING/DISCUSSION TOPICS

1. Describe the role of beta blockers in treating certain types of visceral disorders.

2. At certain times when people are very excited or are shocked suddenly, their bowels and/or urinary sphincters lose control. In terms of the role of the ANS, why does this happen?

3. Some individuals, following a very stressful event such as final exams, frequently come down with colds. Is there any relationship between the ANS, stress, and the onset of an illness? Discuss.

4. Most people feel very tired after they eat a big meal. Why?

5. How can biofeedback be used to reduce effects of constant pain and stress?

6. Why is sympathetic action diffuse and long lasting while parasympathetic is local and short-lived? What would happen to body systems during a stressful situation if these characteristics were reversed? How would anatomy have to be changed?

LIBRARY RESEARCH TOPICS

1. Do all animals have an autonomic nervous system? If so, is it more or less advanced than ours?

2. The ANS regulates peristaltic waves of the GI tract. If the ganglia and/or fibers controlling this activity were damaged, what would happen? What bacterial agents or type of trauma could cause this?

3. Ulcers seem to occur in hypertensive individuals. What are the causes of this problem and what treatment is available?

4. Nicotine and muscarine are substances that bind at specific receptors. What exactly do these receptors look like? Draw out a cell membrane and illustrate how the receptors might look.

AUDIO VISUAL AIDS/COMPUTER SOFTWARE

Films

1. Autonomic Nervous System (IFB, 17 min., C, 1975) Portrays aspects of the autonomic nervous system, with photographs of gastroscopic and bronchoscopic anatomy, of constriction and dilation of the pupils, and the control of body temperature.

2. The Autonomic Nervous System - An Overview (USNAC, 17 min., C, 1973) A general introduction to the human ANS, explaining the basic functions of the two divisions.

Filmstrips/Slides

1. The Autonomic System (PHM)

See *Guide to Audiovisual Resources* at the end of this module for key to AV distributors

LECTURE ENHANCEMENT MATERIAL

CLINICAL AND RELATED TERMS

1. Achalasia - failure to relax the smooth muscle fibers of the gastrointestinal tract, especially of the lower esophagus, due to degeneration of the ganglion cells in the walls of the organ.

2. Belladonna - a deadly nightshade plant, Atropa belladonna. Source of various alkaloids, such as atropine and scopolamine. Used as a sedative and for the management of gastrointestinal disorders.

3. Cardiospasm - a failure to relax the esophagus and an absence of esophageal motility.

4. Gangliosympathectomy - excision of a sympathetic ganglion.

5. Sympathicotripsy - surgical crushing of a sympathetic nerve or ganglion.

6. Sympathectomy - a resection or transection of a sympathetic nerve.

7. Transcendental Meditation - a technique used to attain a state of complete physical and psychological relaxation.

8. Vagotomy - transection of the vagus nerve.

DISORDERS/HOMEOSTATIC IMBALANCES

Tumors

1. Paraganglioma - a tumor of the autonomic nervous system tissue, composed of a collection of chromaffin cells occurring outside the adrenal medulla, usually near the sympathetic ganglia. Most tend to secrete epinephrine or norepinephrine.

2. Sympathicoblastoma - a malignant tumor containing embryonic cells that normally develop into sympathetic nerve cells.

3. Sympathogonioma - a tumor composed of undifferentiated embryonic cells that normally would develop into sympathetic cells.

Hereditary Disorders

1. Familial Dysautonomia - a hereditary condition marked by defective lacrimation, skin blotching, emotional instability, motor incoordination, total absence of pain sensation and hyporeflexia.

Degenerative and Other Disorders

1. Autonomic Dysreflexia - an exaggerated reflex of the autonomic nervous system to stimulation, mainly as a result of spinal cord injury. Condition requires immediate care, especially to correct the high blood pressure as a result of the dysreflexia.

2. Hyperreflexic Bladder - an exaggerated reflex of the bladder due to spinal cord injury or to unknown causes.

3. Olivopontocerebellar Atopy - a degenerative disorder of the neurons around the olive, pons, and cerebellum, as well as the basal ganglia and spinal cord. May also be inherited.

4. Striatonigral Degeneration - atrophy of the putamen and caudate nuclei. Similar to paralysis agitans.

APPLIED PHARMACOLOGY

Drugs for Neurourologic Disorders

1. Bethanechol (Urecholine) - used for the management of urinary retention, including neurogenic atony in the absence of obstruction. Exhibits a selective action on the urinary bladder and gut, but little action on autonomic ganglia.

2. Ephedrine Sulfate - used in treatment of mild-to-moderate sphincteric incontinence. Acts on the alpha adrenergic receptors of the smooth muscle at the bladder, neck and proximal urethra.

3. Oxybutynin C1 (Ditropan) - used to reduce spasm of the digestive system, bladder, and urethra. Acts directly on smooth muscle distal to the cholinergic receptor site.

4. Propantheline Br. (Pro-Banthine) - used in the depression of uninhibited bladder contractions. Antagonizes muscarinic effects of acetylcholine to increase bladder capacity and reduce irritative symptoms.

Drugs Acting at Cholinergic Synapses

1. Anticholinesterases (Edrophonium, Neostigmine, Organophosphates, Physostigmine) - have little effect at ganglia andare used for nicotine effect at the neuromuscular junction. Acts by inhibiting cholinesterase, either reversibly (edrophonium) or irreversibly (organophosphates).

2. Ganglion Blockers (Hexamethonium) - act as a cholinergic receptor antagonist through a cation-channel blocker. Used in the management of hypertensive cardiovascular disease, but especially in the production of controlled hypotension during surgery.

3. Nicotinic and Muscarinic Agonists (Methacholine, Carbachol, Nicotine) - act directly on receptors to increase the parasympathetic effect; exception - heart muscle receptors. (See Marieb, p. 456.)

Drugs Acting on the Sympathetic System

1. Alpha-Adrenoceptor Antagonists (Prazosin, Phentolamine) - act as alpha blockers. Sometimes used in the treatment of hypertension.

2. Beta - Adrenoceptor Antagonists (Propanalol, Timolol, Pindolol) - Act as beta blockers. Used in the treatment of hypertension, angina, and cardiac arrhythmias.

3. Ephedrine - a sympathomimetic amine that acts mainly by causing noradrenaline release. Its effect resembles those of adrenaline, but lasts longer. Appears to be a mild central stimulant.

4. Phenylephrine - used as mydriatics and in decongestant preparation. Is an alpha$_1$ agonist.

5. Solbutamol - a beta$_2$ adrenoceptor agonist that causes bronchial dilation and is used in the treatment of asthma and to relax uterine muscles to prevent preterm labor.

SUGGESTED READINGS

1. Bower, B. "Monkeying With Stress." Science News 125 (Apr. 1984):234-235.

2. Bower, B. "Shaping Up Your Mind." Science News 130 (Aug. 1986).

3. Decara, L.V. "Learning in the Autonomic Nervous System." Scientific American (Jan. 1970).

4. Goldberg, L.I., and S.I. Rajfer. "The Role of Adrenergic and Dopamine Receptors." Hospital Practice (June 1985).

5. Greenberg, J. "Psyching Out Reaches High-Tech Proportions." Science News 127 (May 1985).

6. Hammond, R.E. "Taming The Wild Emotions." Carolina Tips 46 (Oct. 1983).

7. Herbert, W. "Sources of Temperament: Bashful at Birth?" Science News 121 (Jan. 1982).

8. Herbert, W. "Punching the Biological Timeclock." Science News 122 (July 1982).

9. House, M.A. "Cocaine." American Journal of Nursing 90 (Apr. 1990):40-45.

10. Long, M.E. "What is this Thing Called Sleep." National Geographic 172(6) (Dec. 1987):786-782.

11. Mandell, A.J. "Neurobiological Barriers to Euphoria." American Scientist 61 (Oct. 1973).

12. Silberner, J. "Hypnotism Under the Knife." Science News 129 (Mar. 1986).

13. Treichel, J.A. "How Emotions Affect Involuntary Nerves." Science News 124 (Sept. 1983).

14. Wacker, R. "The Good Die Younger." Science 85 (Dec. 1985).

15. Waid, W.M., and M.T. Orne. "The Physiological Detection of Deception." American Scientist 70 (1981).

16. Wallace R.K. and H. Benson "The Physiology of Meditation." Scientific American 226 (Feb. 1972):85-90.

17. Wilbur, R. "A Drug to Fight Cocaine." Science 86 (Mar. 1986).

HANDOUTS

The following section contains prepared handout material which may be photocopied and distributed to the class. All materials are organized so that selected items can be cut and pasted for the instructors individual needs.

If budgets are a limiting factor in the use of handouts, these masters may be placed on reserve in the library for students to photocopy at their convenience.

Preview Of Selected Key Terms

Autonomic nervous system . . . . (auto=self; nom=govern) The efferent division of the peripheral nervous system that innervated cardiac and smooth muscles and glands; also called the involuntary or visceral motor system.

Ganglion . . . . (ganglion=knot on a string, swelling) Collection of nerve cell bodies outside the CNS.

Preganglionic neuron . . . . Autonomic motor neuron that has its cell body in the CNS and projects its axon to a peripheral ganglion.

Postganglionic neuron . . . . Autonomic motor neuron that has its cell body in a peripheral ganglion and projects its axon an effector.

Sympathetic division . . . . (sym=together; pathos=feeling) Division of the autonomic nervous system that activates toe body to cope with some stressor (danger, excitement, etc.); the fight, fright, and flight subdivision.

Parasympathetic . . . . (para=beside, alongside) The division of the autonomic system that oversees digestion, elimination, and glandular function; the resting and digesting subdivision.

Sympathetic tone . . . . State of partial vasoconstriction of the blood vessels maintained by sympathetic fibers.

Terms/Disorders

1. Achalasia - failure to relax the smooth muscle fibers of the gastrointestinal tract, especially of the lower esophagus, due to degeneration of the ganglion cells in the walls of the organ.

2. Alpha-Adrenoceptor Antagonists (Prazosin, Phentolamine) - act as alpha blockers. Sometimes used in the treatment of hypertension.

3. Anticholinesterases (Edrophonium, Neostigmine, Organophosphates, Physostigmine) - have little effect at ganglia andare used for nicotine effect at the neuromuscular junction. Acts by inhibiting cholinesterase, either reversibly (edrophonium) or irreversibly (organophosphates).

4. Autonomic Dysreflexia - an exaggerated reflex of the autonomic nervous system to stimulation, mainly as a result of spinal cord injury. Condition requires immediate care, especially to correct the high blood pressure as a result of the dysreflexia.

5. Belladonna - a deadly nightshade plant, Atropa belladonna. Source of various alkaloids, such as atropine and scopolamine. Used as a sedative and for the management of gastrointestinal disorders.

6. Beta - Adrenoceptor Antagonists (Propanalol, Timolol, Pindolol) - Act as beta blockers. Used in the treatment of hypertension, angina, and cardiac arrhythmias.

7. Bethanechol (Urecholine) - used for the management of urinary retention, including neurogenic atony in the absence of obstruction. Exhibits a selective action on the urinary bladder and gut, but little action on autonomic ganglia.

8. Cardiospasm - a failure to relax the esophagus and an absence of esophageal motility.

9. Ephedrine Sulfate - used in treatment of mild-to-moderate sphincteric incontinence. Acts on the alpha adrenergic receptors of the smooth muscle at the bladder, neck and proximal urethra.

10. Ganglion Blockers (Hexamethonium) - act as a cholinergic receptor antagonist through a cation-channel blocker. Used in the management of hypertensive cardiovascular disease, but especially in the production of controlled hypotension during surgery.

11. Gangliosympathectomy - excision of a sympathetic ganglion.

12. Hyperreflexic Bladder - an exaggerated reflex of the bladder due to spinal cord injury or to unknown causes.

13. Nicotinic and Muscarinic Agonists (Methacholine, Carbachol, Nicotine) - act directly on receptors to increase the parasympathetic effect; exception - heart muscle receptors. (See Marieb, p. 456.)

14. Paraganglioma - a tumor of the autonomic nervous system tissue, composed of a collection of chromaffin cells occurring outside the adrenal medulla, usually near the sympathetic ganglia. Most tend to secrete epinephrine or norepinephrine.

15. Phenylephrine - used as mydriatics and in decongestant preparation. Is an $alpha_1$ agonist.

16. Solbutamol - a $beta_2$ adrenoceptor agonist that causes bronchial dilation and is used in the treatment of asthma and to relax uterine muscles to prevent preterm labor.

Age Associated Changes

General Age Related Changes

-Constipation due to decreased gastrointestinal motility
-Diminished tear formation resulting in dry eyes and frequent eye infections

Decreased Vascular Efficiency

-Decrease in response time of sympathetic vasoconstrictor centers causing fainting
-Trend toward higher systolic and diastolic pressures
-Decreased baroreceptor sensitivity
-Decreased vascular sensitivity to adrenergic agents

Other Body Effects

-Decreased efficiency of body temperature regulation
-Decreased release of fatty acids (by adrenergic stimulation of adipose cells)

MATCHING QUESTIONS

The somatic and autonomic efferent divisions have been compared and contrasted. Identify the motor division described by each phrase.

    a. Autonomic   b. Somatic

    ___ 1. Innervates skeletal muscles.
    ___ 2. Innervates cardiac muscle, smooth muscle, and glands.
    ___ 3. Two neuron efferent chain.
    ___ 4. One neuron efferent chain.
    ___ 5. Nerve cell bodies may be found in the CNS.
    ___ 6. Nerve cell bodies may be found in ganglia.
    ___ 7. Releases only acetylcholine.
    ___ 8. Some of its fibers release acetylcholine; others release norepinephrine.

Qtype:»Memory   Outline:»II.A.   Text pp.»458-459
Answers:»1-b; 2-a; 3-a; 4-b; 5-a,b; 6-a; 7-b; 8-a

Relate each of the following terms or phrases to either the sympathetic or parasympathetic, or both.

    a. Sympathetic   b. Parasympathetic

    ___ 1. Short preganglionic, long postganglionic fibers.
    ___ 2. Prevertebral ganglia.
    ___ 3. Paravertebral ganglia.
    ___ 4. White and gray rami communicantes.
    ___ 5. Thoracolumbar outflow.
    ___ 6. Commonly acts in a widespread and diffuse manner.
    ___ 7. Cholinergic fibers.
    ___ 8. Superior mesenteric and coeliac ganglia.
    ___ 9. Otic and ciliary ganglia.
    ___10. More specific control.
    ___11. Innervates sweat glands.
    ___12. Increases blood pressure.
    ___13. Decreases heart rate.
    ___14. Causes erection of the penis.
    ___15. Stimulates ciliary muscles of the eye.
    ___16. Active after you have eaten a gourmet meal.

Qtype:»Memory   Outline:»III.   Text pp.»460-466
Answers:»1-a; 2-a; d-a; 4-a; 5-a; 6-a; 7-a,b; 8-a; 9-b
10-b; 11-a; 12-a; 13-b; 14-b; 15-b; 16-b

Specify whether acetylcholine (ACh) or norepinephrine (NE) is released at the following nerve endings.

    a. ACh   b. NE

    ___ 1. Preganglionic sympathetic.
    ___ 2. Preganglionic parasympathetic.
    ___ 3. Postganglionic sympathetic to sweat glands.
    ___ 4. Postganglionic parasympathetic.

_____ 5. Most postganglionic sympathetic.

Qtype:»Memory   Outline:»IV.A.1.   Text pp.»466-468
Answers:»1-a; 2-a; 3-a; 4-a; 5-b

TRUE/FALSE QUESTIONS

1. Since the ANS is a visceral motor system, afferent pathways are of no importance and actually are rarely found.
   a. true   b. false

   Qtype:»Concept   Outline:»III.C.   Text pp.»466
   Answers:»false

2. The splanchnic nerves pass through the inferior hypogastric plexus.
   a. true   b. false

   Qtype:»Memory   Outline:»III.A.3.   Text pp.»462
   Answers:»true

3. The gray rami communicantes consist of unmyelinated postganglionic fibers.
   a. true   b. false

   Qtype:»Memory   Outline:»III.B.2.a.   Text pp.»465
   Answers:»true

4. The structures that specifically exhibit vasomotor tone are under sympathetic control only.
   a. true   b. false

   Qtype:»Memory   Outline:»IV.C.3.   Text pp.»468
   Answers:»true

5. The autonomic nervous system is a functional rather than an anatomical division.
   a. true   b. false

   Qtype:»Concept   Outline:»II   Text pp.»458
   Answers:»false

6. The autonomic nervous system may cause activation or inhibition, depending on the division that is active and the target that is affected.
   a. true   b. false

   Qtype:»Concept   Outline:»IV.C.   Text pp.»468
   Answers:»true

7. The coeliac ganglion is primarily associated with the parasympathetic division.
             a. true   b. false

   Qtype:»Memory   Outline:»III.B.3.b   Text pp.»465
   Answers:»false

---

8. Muscarine binding to nicotinic receptors inhibits the effect of the receptor and vice versa.
             a. true   b. false

   Qtype:»Concept   Outline:»IV.A.2.   Text pp.»467
   Answers:»false

---

9. The sympathetic chain is composed of prevertebral ganglia.
             a. true   b. false

   Qtype:»Memory   Outline:»III.B.1.c.   Text pp.»463
   Answers:»false

---

10. Since many of the same cardiac cells are innervated by both parasympathetic and
    sympathetic fibers, the influence of the two divisions on the heart is synergistic.
             a. true   b. false

   Qtype:»Concept   Outline:»IV.C.4.   Text pp.»468
   Answers:»false

---

11. Thermoregulatory responses to increased heat are mediated by the sympathetic nervous
    division.
             a. true   b. false

   Qtype:»Memory   Outline:»IV.C.5.b.   Text pp.»471
   Answers:»true

---

12. Most disorders of the autonomic nervous system reflect abnormalities of smooth muscle
    control.
             a. true   b. false

   Qtype:»Concept   Outline:»V.   Text pp.»472-473
   Answers:»true

---

13. Alpha-adrenergic effects are usually inhibitory.
             a. true   b. false

   Qtype:»Memory   Outline:»IV.A.3.a.   Text pp.»468
   Answers:»false

---

14. The adrenal medulla is considered to be a "misplaced sympathetic ganglion" by some.

     a. true   b. false

  Qtype:»Memory Outline:»III.B.4.   Text pp.»466
  Answers:»true

---

15. The substance released by the axonal endings of the somatic efferent fibers and by the parasympathetic nerve fiber endings, is acetylocholine.

     a. true   b. false

  Qtype:»Memory Outline:»II.A.3.   Text pp.»459
  Answers:»true

---

16. Most body organs are innervated by both the sympathetic and parasympathetic divisions.

     a. true   b. false

  Qtype:»Concept Outline:»IV.C.1..   Text pp.»468
  Answers:»true

---

17. Autonomic reflex centers occur in the spinal cord, medulla, and midbrain, but generally **not** the hypothalamus.

     a. true   b. false

  Qtype:»Memory Outline:»IV.D.2.   Text pp.»472
  Answers:»false

---

18. Through direct neural stimulation, the sympathetic division promotes many metabolic effects via hormone release.

     a. true   b. false

  Qtype:»Concept Outline:»IV.C.5.d.   Text pp.»471
  Answers:»true

---

19. The receptors found on the heart include both beta adrenergic and muscarinic receptors.

     a. true   b. false

  Qtype:»Memory Outline:»IV.A.   Text pp.»467
  Answers:»true

MULTIPLE-CHOICE QUESTIONS

1. The secretions of the adrenal medulla act to supplement the effects of:
   a. parasympathetic innervation.
   b. sympathetic stimulation.
   c. vagus nerve activity.
   d. reflex control.
   e. neurosecretory substances.

   Qtype:»Concept   Outline:»III.B.3.b.   Text pp.»466
   Answers:»b

2. In contrast to the somatic nervous system, the autonomic nervous system:
   a. has two efferent neurons.
   b. has two afferent neurons.
   c. stimulates its effector cells.
   d. has both afferent and efferent fibers.

   Qtype:»Memory   Outline:»II.A.2.   Text pp.»458
   Answers:»a

3. Preparing the body for the "fight or flight" response is the role of the:
   a. sympathetic nervous system.
   b. cerebrum.
   c. parasympathetic nervous system.
   d. None of the above are correct.

   Qtype:»Concept   Outline:»II.B.1.   Text pp.»459
   Answers:»a

4. The parasympathetic nervous system is characterized by peripheral ganglia near the:
   a. organs with short postganglionic fibers.
   b. organs with long postganglionic fibers.
   c. spinal cord with short postganglionic fibers.
   d. spinal cord with long postganglionic fibers.

   Qtype:»Memory   Outline:»III.A.1.b.   Text pp.»460
   Answers:»a

5. Sympathetic fibers leave the spinal cord in the:
   a. craniosacral regions, and the postganglionic fibers secrete norepinephrine.
   b. thoracolumbar region and the postganglionic fibers secrete acetylcholine.
   c. craniosacral region and the postganglionic fibers secrete acetylcholine.
   d. thoracolumbar region and the postganglionic fibers secrete norepinephrine.

   Qtype:»Memory   Outline:»III.B.   Text pp.»463-466
   Answers:»d

6. A drug that might be used to specifically reduce heart rate in cardiac patients could be:
    a. anticholinesterase.
    c. adrenergic.
    b. epinephrine.
    d. a beta blocker.

> Qtype:»Memory   Outline:»IV.B.   Text pp.»468
> Answers:»d

7. The parasympathetic ganglion that serves the eye is the:
    a. ciliary ganglion.
    c. submandibular ganglion.
    b. sphenopalatine ganglion.
    d. otic ganglion.

> Qtype:»Memory   Outline:»III.A.2.a.   Text pp.»460
> Answers:»a

8. Where would you **not** find an autonomic ganglion?
    a. in the head
    d. in the abdomen
    b. in the cervical region
    e. in the armpit
    c. close to the visceral effectors they serve

> Qtype:»Memory   Outline:»III.A.1.   Text pp.»460
> Answers:»e

9. Trigeminal nerves have the broadest facial distribution of all the cranial nerves:
    a. facial.
    d. trigeminal.
    b. glossopharyngeal.
    e. vagus.
    c. oculomotor.

> Qtype:»Memory   Outline:»III.A.2.   Text pp.»462
> Answers:»d

10. Cardiovascular effects of the sympathetic division include all but:
    a. constriction of most blood vessels.
    b. dilation of the vessels serving the skeletal muscles.
    c. increase of heart rate and force.
    d. dilation of the blood vessels serving the skin and digestive viscera.

> Qtype:»Concept   Outline:»IV.C.   Text pp.»468
> Answers:»d

11. The sympathetic system causes:
    a. decreased blood glucose, increased peristalsis, increased heart rate and blood pressure.
    b. increased blood glucose and peristalsis and decreased heart rate and blood pressure.
    c. increased blood glucose, heart rate, and blood pressure and decreased peristalsis.
    d. decreased blood glucose, heart rate, and blood pressure, and increased peristalsis.

> Qtype:»Concept   Outline:»IV.C.5.   Text pp.»471
> Answers:»c

12. Over 90 percent of all parasympathetic fibers are derived from cranial nerve number:
    a. III.
    b. V.
    c. VII.
    d. X.
    e. XII.

    Qtype:»Memory   Outline:»III.A.2.   Text pp.»461
    Answers:»d

___

13. The "resting and digesting" division of the autonomic nervous system is:
    a. the parasympathetic division.
    b. the sympathetic division.
    c. the somatic division.
    d. the peripheral nervous system.

    Qtype:»Concept   Outline:»II.B.2.   Text pp.»459
    Answers:»a

___

14. Control of temperature, endocrine activity, hunger,and thirst, are functions associated with the:
    a. medulla.
    b. cerebellum.
    c. hypothalamus.
    d. thalamus.

    Qtype:»Memory   Outline:»IV.D.2.   Text pp.»472
    Answers:»c

___

15. Which of these effectors is **not** directly controlled by the autonomic nervous system?
    a. smooth muscle
    b. cardiac muscle
    c. skeletal muscle
    d. most glands

    Qtype:»Memory   Outline:»II.A.   Text pp.»458
    Answers:»c

___

16. Which of the following is **not** a result of parasympathetic stimulation?
    a. salivation
    b. constriction of the pupils
    c. increased peristalsis of the digestive viscera
    d. relaxation of the urethral sphincter
    e. all are related to parasympathetic division

    Qtype:»Concept   Outline:»IV.C.   Text pp.»468
    Answers:»e

___

17. The smooth muscle of the digestive viscera is served largely by the:
    a. lumbar splanchnic nerves.
    b. coeliac plexus.
    c. the pelvic nerves.
    d. tenth cranial nerve.

    Qtype:»Memory   Outline:»III.A.2.d.   Text pp.»461
    Answers:»d

___

18. The route of major parasympathetic outflow from the head is:
    a. the sympathetic trunk.
    b. phrenic nerve.
    c. vagus nerve.
    d. sacral nerve.
    e. trigeminal nerve.

Qtype:»Memory   Outline:»III.A.2.d.   Text pp.»461
Answers:»c

19. The site of origin of the preganglionic fibers of the parasympathetic nervous system is:
    a. the thoracolumbar region of the spinal cord.
    b. the higher brain centers.
    c. the sympathetic chain.
    d. the brain stem and the sacral region of the cord.

Qtype:»Memory   Outline:»III.A.1.   Text pp.»460
Answers:»d

20. Sympathetic responses generally are widespread because:
    a. inactivation of norepinephrine by uptake into the neuron is fairly slow.
    b. multiple synapses are made with postganglionic neurons by single preganglionic axons.
    c. preganglionic fibers are short.
    d. preganglionic fibers are long.

Qtype:»Concept   Outline:»IV.C.6.a.   Text pp.»471
Answers:»b

21. Possible locations for the cell bodies of autonomic preganglionic neurons include:
        1. the brain
        2. the spinal cord
        3. autonomic ganglia
    a. 1 only
    b. 2 only
    c. 3 only
    d. 1 and 2
    e. 2 and 3

Qtype:»Memory   Outline:»II.A.1.   Text pp.»458
Answers:»d

22. Autonomic ganglia contain:
    a. an outer connective tissue capsule around the cell bodies of preganglionic motor neurons.
    b. synapses between postganglionic fibers and their effectors.
    c. the cell bodies of motor neurons.
    d. only efferent fibers.
    e. both somatic afferent and efferent neurons.

Qtype:»Concept   Outline:»II.A.2.   Text pp.»459
Answers:»c

23. Examples of sympathetic function include
    1. dilation of cardiac and skeletal muscle blood vessels during exercise.
    2. an increase in smooth muscle activity in the digestive tract.
    3. constriction of the pupil of the eye.
    a. 1 only
    b. 2 only
    c. 3 only
    d. 1 and 3
    e. 2 and 3

Qtype:»Concept   Outline:»II.B.2.   Text pp.»459-460
Answers:»a

---

24. Parasympathetic functions include:
    a. a stimulation of heart rate and force of contraction.
    b. allowing the body to cope with an external threat.
    c. dilation of blood vessels to the skin.
    d. increasing urinary tract motility.
    e. mobilizing storage energy sources.

Qtype:»Concept   Outline:»II.B.1.   Text pp.»459
Answers:»c

---

25. Fibers that enter and leave the sympathetic chain without synapsing form structures called:
    a. white rami communicantes
    b. gray rami communicantes
    c. spinal nerves
    d. splanchnic nerves
    e. sympathetic trunk.

Qtype:»Memory   Outline:»III.B.2.   Text pp.»465
Answers:»d

---

26. The vagus nerve contribures to which of the following plexuses?
    1. cardiac
    2. pulmonary
    3. esophageal
    a. 1 only
    b. 2 only
    c. 3 only
    d. 1 and 3
    e. 1, 2 and 3

Qtype:»Memory   Outline:»III.A.2.d.   Text pp.»462
Answers:»e

27. If an individual is given an anticholinesterase compound, what possible effects could result?
    1. increased heart rate and force of contraction.
    2. an increase in the fight or flight response.
    3. prolonged action of ACh.
    a. 1 only   d. 1 and 3
    b. 2 only   e. 2 and 3
    c. 3 only

Qtype:»Concept   Outline:»IV.B.   Text pp.»468
Answers:»c

28. Visceral reflex arcs differ from somatic in that:
    a. Visceral arcs contain two sensory neurons.
    b. Somatic arcs contain one additional component that visceral arcs do not possess.
    c. Visceral arcs involve two motor neurons.
    d. Visceral arcs do not use integration centers.
    e. None of the above are correct.

Qtype:»Concept   Outline:»IV.D.1.   Text pp.»471
Answers:»c

29. Parasympathetic tone involves:
    1. constant low level stimulation to visceral organs.
    2. determination of the normal level of digestive and urinary system function.
    3. parasympathetic domination of heart action.
    a. 1 only   d. 1 and 3
    b. 2 only   e. 1, 2 and 3
    c. 3 only

Qtype:»Concept   Outline:»IV.C.4.   Text pp.»469
Answers:»e

30. Which of the following is most correct?
    a. Most spinal nerves contain both somatic and autonomic fibers.
    b. Most body responses to changing internal and external environments involve both enhanced skeletal muscle and visceral sctivity.
    c. Somatic and autonomic branches are not truly individual entities, function is well integrated.
    d. Higher brain centers regulate both somatic and autonomic function.
    e. All the above are correct.

Qtype:»Concept   Outline:»II.A.4.   Text pp.»459
Answers:»e

SHORT-ANSWER QUESTIONS

1. How is hypertension and the ANS related?

> Qtype:»Concept   Outline:»V.A.   Text pp.»472
> Answers:»The ANS is involved with nearly every process that goes on within the body.
> Since it controls smooth muscle activity, the heart, and blood vessel constriction, it is not
> surprising that hypertension and ANS activity are related. Over production of adrenergic
> responses for extended periods keeps vessels constricted and heart rate and force of
> contraction high. This can lead to hypertension. This is many times stress related, and
> can be treated with adrenergic blocking agents.

2. What effect does aging have on the ANS?

> Qtype:»Concept   Outline:»VI.C.   Text pp.»473
> Answers:»During youth, most ANS malfunctions are the result of injury. In old age, ANS
> efficiendy decreases. Constipation (due to G.I. motility decline), dry eyes, and frequent
> eye infections can occur. Fainting may occur due to slow responding vasomotor centers.
> These problems can be controlled by behavior modification.

3. Describe three paths a preganglionic sympathetic fiber may take to reach its synapse point
   with the postganglionic neuron.

> Qtype:»Memory   Outline:»III.B.   Text pp.»463-466
> Answers:»It can synapse with a postganglionic neuron in the paravertebral ganglion;
> ascend or descend within the chain to synapse in another ganglion; or pass through the
> sympathetic chain and synapse in a collateral ganglion.

4. What studies have suggested that the ANS can also be subject to voluntary controls?

> Qtype:»Concept   Outline:»IV.D.3.   Text pp.»460
> Answers:»Experimentation involving meditation and biofeedback have indicated that this
> is possible. Meditating yogis have indicated major physiological states, while biofeedback
> training suggests that we can alter certain processes such as heart rate, blood pressure,
> and muscle tone.

CLINICAL QUESTIONS

1. Richard has been under great stress and has complained of migraine headaches for weeks. He tried all kinds of drugs with little effect. When he was at the end of his rope, a friend suggested yoga and meditation. Having nothing to lose, he tried it and after two weeks, felt like a new person. How could this help him?

> Qtype:»Application Outline:»IV.D.3.a.   Text pp.»472
> Answers:»Meditation and biofeedback techniques seem to cause the patient to enter a
> physiological state of concentration where sympathetic induced hypertension can be
> reduced. By concentrating on relaxing thoughts, heart and respiratory rates can be
> reduced. The effects are more widespread than can be explained by parasympathetic
> influences so the control could be consciously induced.

2. Mark, a rather obese couch potato, likes to eat a very big meal in the evening. After the meal his wife would like him to help clean up the dishes, but John explains that he is "too tired" and promptly goes to sleep. What seems to be his problem?

> Qtype:»Application Outline:»II.B.   Text pp.»459-460
> Answers:»After a meal, parasympathetic influences dominate which increase digestive
> functions while decreasing cardiac and respiratory activity which causes the individual to
> feel sleepy.

3. Carla, a very emotional young girl, was suddenly startled by an extremely loud bang which sounded like a gunshot. Her heartbeat accelerated rapidly. When she found that the noise was only a car backfiring, she felt greatly relieved but her heart kept beating heavily for over half an hour. Why did this happen?

> Qtype:»Application Outline:»IV.C.6.   Text pp.»471
> Answers:»The effects of sympathetic activators are logn lasting since norepinephrine is
> inactivated slowly. Also, the adrenal medulla releases this neurotransmitter which adds to
> the long-lasting effects of adrenergic stimulation.

4. Ms. Johnson, an automobile whiplash victim, has been suffering spinal shock but is looking forward to complete recovery. One night on evening rounds, her nurse discovered her in a fetel position, her body drenched with sweat. She was incontinent of feces and urine and her blood pressure was dangerously high (over 200 mm Hg). After awhile she was stabilized. How could these events happen and what is this response called?

> Qtype:»Application Outline:»V.C.   Text pp.»473
> Answers:»The mass reflex reaction is a life threatening condition involving both somatic
> and autonomic nerves in most quadriplegics and victims of spinal shock. The symptoms
> can precipitate a stroke.

Neural Integration

15

CHAPTER PREVIEW

This chapter explores the sensory and motor pathways, how they integrate with our higher learning centers, and how they are processed. Activities such as walking, running, and posture will be examined in detail to illustrate how they are accomplished. The last portion of this chapter looks at how we think, remember and relate to others. The concepts of sleep, wakefulness, and memory will be explained.

AT A GLANCE

INTEGRATING THE PACKAGE

SUGGESTED LECTURE OUTLINE

I. Sensory Integration: From Reception to Perception (pp. 476-479)
    A. Introduction (p. 476)
    B. General Organization of the Somatosensory System (pp. 477-479)
        1. General Characteristics
        2. Processing at the Receptor Level
        3. Processing at the Circuit Level
            a. Basic Features

REVIEW ITEMS

1. Neuronal integration, (Chapter 11, pp. 370-373)

2. Diencephalon, (Chapter 12, pp. 392-394)

3. Limbic system, (Chapter 12, p. 400)

4. Thalamus, (Chapter 12, p. 392)

5. Hypothalamus, (Chapter 12, p. 394)

6. Ascending spinocerebellar tracts, (Chapter 12, p. 411)

7. Reticular activating system, (Chapter 12, p. 402)

8. Lateral and anterior spinocerebellar tracts, (Chapter 12, p. 411)

9. Descending tracts of the spinal cord, (Chapter 12, p. 414)

10. Spinal roots, (Chapter 12, p. 409)

11. Gray and white mater of the spinal cord, (Chapter 12, p. 409)

12. Cerebellum, (Chapter 12, pp. 398-400)

13. Basal nuclei, (Chapter 12, p. 392)

14. Receptor and generator potentials, (Chapter 13, p. 425)

15. General reflexes, (Chapter 13, pp. 447-453)

16. Sensory receptors, (Chapter 13, pp. 424-426)

ANSWERS TO TEXTBOOK CHAPTER QUESTIONS

Multiple Choice/Matching

1. c

2. d

3. c

4. e

5. b

6. (1)d; (2)e; (3)d; (4)a

Short Answer Essay Questions

7. Sensation means awareness of changes in the internal and external environment. Perception means conscious interpretation of those sensations. (p. 476)

8. Analytic discrimination means that each quality retains its individual nature. Synthetic discrimination means that the qualities merge together creating a new sensation with new properties. (p. 479)

9. a. CPGs are local circuits that control locomotion; may involve networks of spinal cord neurons arranged in reverberating circuits.
   b. CPGs are controlled by command neurons, interneurons located at the projection level of the motor hierarchy, expecially the brain stem. (p. 482)

10. See Fig. 15.3, p. 482, for a diagram of the hierarchy of motor control.

11. The direct system involves neurons of the large pyramidal tracts that synapse in the cord and mainly produce fine or skilled voluntary muscle contractions of the distal muscles of the limbs. The indirect system involves neurons of the reticular, vestibular, and red nuclei that are mainly involved in involuntary movements of the proximal muscles of the limbs and trunk muscles that act in, posture and arm-swinging, for example. (p. 483)

12. They control the outputs of the cortex and brainstem motor centers and stand at the highest level of motor hierarchy. (pp. 483-484)

13. An EEG is a record of the electrical activity of cortical neurons made by using electrodes placed at different locations on the scalp. (p. 485)

14. REM sleep occupies about 50% of the total sleeping time in infants, but then declines with age to stabilize at 25%. Stage 4 sleep declines steadily from birth and disappears completely in those over 60 years. The elderly often remain in a perpetual state of light sleep. (p. 488)

15. a. Narcolepsy means lapsing involuntarily into sleep during waking hours. Insomnia is the inability to obtain the amount or quality of sleep needed.
    b. Narcoleptics seem to have a problem controlling circuits involved with REM sleep. In the evening sleep they spend little time in REM cycle hence they may not be acquiring enough REM sleep at night. Their narcoleptic episodes indicate REM sleep.
    c. Sleep episodes can occur at any time without warning which would be dangerous if the person was driving or using a power saw, for example. (p. 488)

16. a. Epilepsy is a disorder characterized by abnormal electrical discharges of groups of brain neurons.
    b. Petit mal seen with children is the least severe involvong only temporary lapses of attentiveness. Grand mal is most severe, involving loss of consciousness and intense convulsions. (p 486)

17. Flashes of light, sensory hallucinations of taste or smell that sometimes occur prior to an epileptic seizure. (p. 486)

18. Holistic processing supposes that consciousness involves simultaneous activity of large areas of the cerebral cortex, that consciousness is superimposed on other types of neural activity, and that consciousness is totally interconnected. (p. 489)

19. STM is fleeting memory that serves as a sort of temporary holding bin for data and is limited to seven or eight chunks of data. LTM seems to have unlimited capacity for storage and is very long lasting unless altered. (pp. 489-490)

20. a. Emotional state, rehearsal, association of new information with information already stored, automatic memory. (p. 490)
    b. Memory consolidation involves fitting new facts into the network of preexisting consolidated knowledge stored in the cerebral cortex. (p. 490)

21. Fact memory is the ability to learn explicit information and is related to our conscious thoughts and our ability to manipulate symbols and language. Skill memory is concerned with motor activities acquired through practice. (p. 490)

22. One function cannot exist without the other. To even speak a word, one must choose words that fit, use grammar to organize the words and activate the muscles for speech, all in a split second. Therefore, the process cannot be entirely under conscious control. Nor can it be entirely reflexive, because it is often so original. Diseases such as aphasia help to illustrate this interrelationship. (p. 493)

Critical Thinking and Application Questions

1. a. Direct system; inferior precentral gyrus on the left, Broca's area, and the adjacent premotor area, also other frontal lobe language areas. (p. 483, 492-493)
   b. Abdominal reflexes absent: Babinski's sign present. (p. 483)
   c. Speech apraxia or motor aphasia. (p. 493)

2. Rubbing the back may stimulate more A beta fibers which effectively closes the "gate" (counterirritant theory), thus reducing the pain perception. (p. 481)

3. a. Parkinson's disease.
   b. Basal nuclei, substantia nigra; inadequate dopamine synthesis.

c. Treat with the drug L-dopa. (p. 485)

LABORATORY CORRELATIONS

1. Marieb, E. N. <u>Human Anatomy and Physiology Laboratory Manual; Cat and Fetal Pig Versions</u>. 3rd. ed. Benjamin/Cummings, 1989.

    Exercise 21: General Sensations

2. Marieb, E. N. <u>Human Anatomy and Physiology Laboratory Manual; Brief Version</u>. 3rd. ed. Benjamin/Cummings, 1992.

    Exercise 20: General Sensations

OVERHEAD TRANSPARENCIES INDEX

Transparency	Description
15.3	Hierarchy of motor control

BLACK LINE MASTER INDEX

No Black Line Masters for Chapter 15.

INSTRUCTIONAL AIDS

LECTURE HINTS

1. Clearly distinguish between sensation and perception.

2. Since Chapter 15 relates to several previous chapters, refer students to specific areas for review.

3. Students sometimes are confused with the process of transduction and the relationship between receptor potentials, generator potentials, and action potentials.

4. Emphasize the distinction between processing at the circuit level and processing at the perceptual level.

5. This is section of the course is an ideal opportunity to integrate the information from Chapters 11-14 so that students can pull together many concepts and get an overall sense of how the nervous system functions.

6. Fixed-action patterns are almost like the subroutines of a computer program, once initiated will procede to conclusion. This example can be used to relate information many students have some foundation in (conputers) with new information (processing).

7. Use examples of homeostatis imbalances to reinforce the information concerning normal function.

8. Thoroughly explain how the electrical activity described by brain waves is measured. Students often do not realize that it is the total electrical activity of the brain being measured at the surface of the body and not that of individual neurons, and therefore activity should not look like an action potential.

9. Memory is fascinating to most students, and it is worthwhile to spend some time on the proposed mechanisms.

DEMONSTRATIONS/ACTIVITIES

1. Film(s) or other audiovisual materials of choice.

2. Select a male volunteer to perform a two-point threshold test. Compare his sensitivity with that of a female volunteer.

3. Connect an EEG to a volunteer to exhibit normal brain wave patterns.

4. There are various tests for long- and short-term memory. Present your students with a series of numbers or words and, after a period of time, see how many have recalled the sequence.

5. Conscious thought, memory, and language are inextricably interwoven. Have the students repeat a sequence of words, then have them write down those processes they felt were necessary to listen, interpret, formulate, and repeat the words (or actions).

CRITICAL THINKING/DISCUSSION TOPICS

1. Why can we say that pain is "merely a figment of one's imagination?"

2. How can the study of brain waves be used to diagnose disorders of the brain?

3. Sensory deprivation seems to have a great effect on individuals, physiologically and psychologically. What seems to be the basis for this? When we developed in the womb, were we not deprived of sensory input? Or were we?

4. How can some individuals have a higher pain tolerance than others?

5. Lie detector machines have been used for decades. In view of sensory and motor integrative functions, how and why do they work?

6. Thomas Edison never slept for an extended period of time, but always took "catnaps." Is this healthy and more productive? How much sleep do we really need?

LIBRARY RESEARCH TOPICS

1. Some individuals that have lost a limb experience a phenomenon called "phantom limb" pain. What methods of treatment are available for these individuals?

2. Bradykinin has been found to be a potent pain inducer. What chemicals have been found to counteract this chemical?

3. What are the current theories for the mechanism of action of acupuncture?

4. Some individuals with Parkinson's disease, when receiving treatment with L-dopa, experience schizophrenia. What seems to be the relationship between Parkinson's disease and behavior changes?

5. Some researchers indicate that we experience "circadian rhythms." How are these rhythms coordinated and do we really have them? Do they occur in other animals?

AUDIO VISUAL AIDS/COMPUTER SOFTWARE

Films

1. The Sensory World (CRM, 1971, 33 min., C) Animation scenes demonstrating eyes, ears, sense of touch, and proprioception.

2. The Secrets of Sleep (UI, 53 min., C)

3. Acupuncture: An Exploration (UI, 17 min., C)

4. Acupuncture: Anesthesia (UI, 44 min., C)

5. Pain (TL, 30 min., C)

6. Drugs and the Nervous System (CF, 18 min., C, 1973) Explains in animation how drugs affect the CNS and other organs.

7. Miracle of the Mind (MGHT, 19 min., 1975) Describes the attempts to understand the nature of the mind by surveying the contributions of science.

8. The Muscle Spindle (JW, 19 min., C, 1970) Describes the proprioceptive activity of the muscle spindle and how it responds to muscle movement and tension.

9. The Mind of Man (IU, 119 min., C, 1971) Comprehensive survey of recent mind research, including areas of mind development in children, effects of drugs, dreams, brain structure, chemical changes within the brain, etc.

10. Mind Over Body (TL, 49 min., C, 1973) This film examines techniques that teach patients to use their minds to ward off or cure illness and looks at new areas of research in this area.

11. The Split Brain and Conscious Experience (HR, 17 min., C, 1977) Shows the surgery and testing procedures used on people whose brains have been surgically split to control severe epilepsy.

Filmstrips/Slides

1. Touch, Taste, and Smell (EI, SS-0345F, Filmstrip or Slides) Current theories on neural receptors.

2. Theater of the Night: The Science of Sleep and Dreams, Parts 1-3 (HRM)

Videotapes

1. Memory: Fabric of the Mind (FHS, QB-1738, 28 min., C, VHS/BETA) Program describes recent research on memory, brain chemistry, etc.

2. Dreams: Theater of the Mind (FHS, QB-1737, 28 min., C, VHS/BETA) Program examines theories about dreams.

3. Dream Voyage (FHS, QB-824, 26 min., C, VHS/BETA) Programs study recent experimentation on sleep.

4. As If By A Stroke Of Lightning - A Program About Epilepsy (TF, 36 min., C) The video helps to educate the patient, family, employer, and general public about epilepsy.

See *Guide to Audiovisual Resources* at the end of this module for key to AV distributors

LECTURE ENHANCEMENT MATERIAL

CLINICAL AND RELATED TERMS

1. Acataphasia - an inability to express thoughts in a connected manner because of a central lesion.

2. Acrasia - lack of self-control.

3. Amnesia - loss of memory.

4. Causalgia - a burning pain, often associated with skin changes in the hand or foot, caused by peripheral nerve damage.

5. Chorea - St. Vitus's dance.

6. Echolalia - meaningless repetition of words.

7. Hyperalgesia - excessive sensitivity to pain.

8. Megalomania - delusions of grandeur.

9. Misanthropia - hatred of mankind.

10. POSTS - positive occipital sharp transients of sleep.

11. Spindles - a particular wave form in the electroencephalogram during sleep exhibited by short bursts of 12-14 hertz activity.

12. St. Vitus's Dance (Sydenham's Chorea) - a disorder of the CNS that is a manifestation of rheumatic fever, marked by purposeless, irregular movements of voluntary muscles.

13. Stereognosis - the sense by which the form of objects is perceived.

14. Transcutaneous Electrical Nerve Stimulation (TENS) - the placement of electrodes on the body surface directly over nerve fibers that transmit pain. Stimulation of the area appears to relieve pain transmission.

DISORDERS/HOMEOSTATIC IMBALANCES

---

1. Korsakoff's Psychosis - a psychosis generally associated with chronic alcoholism and a vitamin-B deficiency. The psychosis exhibits retrograde and anterograde amnesia, disorientation, lack of insight into the memory deficit, and polyneuritis.

APPLIED PHARMACOLOGY

General Anesthetics

1. Ether - a non-toxic, safe anesthetic agent that is rarely used because of its irritating, nauseating, and inflammatory properties.

2. Halothane - a potent inhalation anesthetic that is non- irritating, causes a concentration-dependent hypotension, and a depression of the respiratory center. Depresses neuronal transmission, causing stage III surgical anesthesia.

3. Isoflurane - a potent inhalation anesthetic that has similar action to halothane, but is less cardiodepressant.

4. Nitrous Oxide - used as a non-inflammable carrier gas for volatile agents since it is not potent enough to use as a sole anesthetic agent. A good analgesic in childbirth, oral surgery, and others.

5. Scopolamine - used in premedication to prevent salivation and bronchial secretions and to protect the heart from arrhythmias.

6. Thiopentone - injected intravenously to induce anesthesia. Acts in less than 30 seconds because the lipid-soluble drug quickly dissolves in the rapidly perfused brain.

Antiepileptic Drugs

1. Clonazepam (Clonapin) - used in the treatment of myoclonic seizures, atonic seizures, absence and akinetic seizures. The drug potentiates the action of gamma aminobutyric acid.

2. Diazepam (Valium) - used as the drug of choice for generalized tonic-chronic seizures. Action similar to clonazepam.

3. Ethosuximide (Zarontin) - used in the treatment of absences and myoclonic seizures. Mechanism of action unknown.

4. Phenobarbital - used for generalized tonic-chronic seizures. Acts by inhibiting synaptic transmission at all levels of the CNS.

5. Phenytoin (Dilantin) - used for generalized tonic-clonic seizures. Acts by inhibiting posttetanic potentiation by membrane stabilization.

Anti-Parkinsonism Drugs

1. Cycrimine HCI (Pagitane) - used in the adjunct treatment of all forms of Parkinsonism. Appears to reduce acetylcholine excess relative to dopamine deficiency in the corpus striatum.

2. L-dopa (Sinemet) - see Marieb, p. 485.

Antidepressant Drugs

1. Amitriptyline (Elavil) - a tricyclic antidepressant with high sedative properties, commonly used for very agitated patients. Acts by blocking the muscarinic, alpha-receptors and histamine receptors.

2. Maprotiline - a non-tricyclic antidepressant whose action is similar to amitriptyline, but has fewer autonomic side-effects.

3. Phenelzine - a monoamine oxidase inhibitor, but may cause severe side effects and is rarely used. Acts to increase the reuptake of amine transmitters.

Drugs Used in Psychosis-Neuroleptics

1. Chlorpromazine (Largactil, Promapar) - used to stop nausea and vomiting, and to reduce anxiety and agitation. Suppresses the brain vomiting center and limbic system by blocking dopamine receptors of the D-2 type in the mesolimbic system. Very sedative, moderate anticholinergic.

2. Fluphenazine (Moditen) - used to stop nausea, vomiting, and to reduce anxiety and agitation. Moderately sedative, very anticholinergic. Action similar to above.

3. Thioridazine - used to stop nausea and vomiting and to reduce anxiety and agitation. Less sedative, less anticholinergic, but more pronounced extrapyramidal effects. Action similar to above.

SUGGESTED READINGS

1. Altman, J. "The Intricate Wiring That Lets Us Move." New Scientist 10 (Mar. 1990):60-63.

2. Alkon, D.L. "Memory Storage and Neural Systems." Scientific American 261 (Jul. 1989):42-50.

3. Binkley, S.A., et al. "The Pineal Gland: A Biological Clock in Vitro." Science 202 (1978):1198.

4. Bower, B. "Neuroleptic Backlash." Science News 128 (July 1985):45-46.

5. Bower, B. "Million-Cell Memories." Science News 130 (Nov. 1986):313-315.

6. Carney, R.M. "Clinical Applications of Relaxation Training." Hospital Practice (July 1983).

7. Erickson, R.P. "On the Neural Bases of Behavior." American Scientist 72 (May-June 1984).

8. Ericsson, K.A., and W.G. Chase. "Exceptional Memory." American Scientist 70 (Nov.-Dec. 1982).

9. Evarts, E.V. "Brain Mechanisms of Movement." Scientific American 241 (Sept. 1979):164-179.

10. Geschwind, N. "Language and the Brain." Scientific American (Apr. 1972:76-83.

11. Gould, J.L., and P. Marler. "Learning by Instinct." Scientific American 256 (Jan. 1987):74-85.

12. Herbert, W. "Forgotten Dreams." Science News 124 (1983):188.

13. Kiester, W. "Spare Parts for Damaged Brains." Science 86 7 (Mar. 1986):33-38.

14. Kindel, S. "Give Me A Bowl Of Texas Chili." Forbes (Sept. 1985):184-186.

15. Loftus, E.F. "The Malleability of Human Memory." American Scientist 67 (May-June 1979):312-320

16. Long, M.E. "What is This Thing Called Sleep." National Geographic 172 (Dec. 1987):787-821.

17. McKean, K. "New Parts for Damaged Brains." Discover 5 (Feb. 1984):68-72.

18. Miller, G.A., and P.M. Gildea. "How Children Learn Words." Scientific American 257 (Sept. 1987):94-99.

19. Mischkin, M., and T. Appenzeller. "The Anatomy of Memory." Scientific American 256 (June 1987):80-89.

20. Montgomery, G. "Molecules of Memory." Discover 10 (Dec. 1989):46-55.

21. Montgomery, G. "The Mind in Motion." Discover (Mar 1989):58-68.

22. Morrison, A.R. "A Window in the Sleeping Brain." Scientific American 248 (Apr. 1983):94-102.

23. Motley, M.T. "Slips of the Tongue." Scientific American 253 (Sept. 1985):116-127.

24. Pearson, K. "The Control of Walking." Scientific American (Dec. 1976):72-86.

25. Regan, D. "Electrical Responses Evoked From the Human Brain." Scientific American 241 (Dec. 1979):134-145.

26. Seyle, H. Stress in Health and Disease. London:Butterworth, 1976.

27. Sperry, R. "Some Effects of Disconnecting the Cerebral Hemispheres." Science 217 (1982):1223.

28. Tulving, E. "Remembering and Knowing the Past." American Scientist 77 (Jul., Aug. 1989):361-367.

29. Weiss, R. "Bypassing the Brain." Science News 136 (Dec. 1989):136,379.

30. West, B.A. "Understanding Endorphins, Our Natural Pain Relief System." Nursing 81 11 (Feb. 1981):50-53.

31. Winter, P.M., and J.N. Miller. "Anesthesiology." Scientific American 252 (Apr. 1985):124-131.

32. Wolff, B.B. "Perceptions of Pain." The Sciences (July-Aug. 1980):10-13, 28.

HANDOUTS

The following section contains prepared handout material which may be photocopied and distributed to the class. All materials are organized so that selected items can be cut and pasted for the instructors individual needs.

If budgets are a limiting factor in the use of handouts, these masters may be placed on reserve in the library for students to photocopy at their convenience.

Preview Of Selected Key Terms

Sensation . . . . Awareness of internal and external events.

Perception . . . . Assigning a meaning to sensation.

Receptor Potential . . . . A graded potential that occurs at a sensory receptor membrane.

Sensory transduction . . . . Conversion of stimulus energy into a nerve impulse.

Command neuron . . . . An interneuron located in a brain stem extrapyramidal nucleus that helps regulate the spinal cord motor circuits.

Synergy . . . . (synerg=work together, cooperate) Coordinated activity of agonist and antagonist muscles that results in smooth, well controlled movements.

Brain waves . . . . Patterns of electrical activity of the neurons of the brain, recordable with an electroencephalograph.

Terms/Disorders

1. Amitriptyline (Elavil) - a tricyclic antidepressant with high sedative properties, commonly used for very agitated patients. Acts by blocking the muscarinic, alpha-receptors and histamine receptors.

2. Amnesia - loss of memory.

3. Chlorpromazine (Largactil, Promapar) - used to stop nausea and vomiting, and to reduce anxiety and agitation. Suppresses the brain vomiting center and limbic system by blocking dopamine receptors of the D-2 type in the mesolimbic system. Very sedative, moderate anticholinergic.

4. Clonazepam (Clonapin) - used in the treatment of myoclonic seizures, atonic seizures, absence and akinetic seizures. The drug potentiates the action of gamma aminobutyric acid.

5. Cycrimine HCI (Pagitane) - used in the adjunct treatment of all forms of Parkinsonism. Appears to reduce acetylcholine excess relative to dopamine deficiency in the corpus striatum.

6. Diazepam (Valium) - used as the drug of choice for generalized tonic-chronic seizures. Action similar to clonazepam.

7. Ether - a non-toxic, safe anesthetic agent that is rarely used because of its irritating, nauseating, and inflammatory properties.

8. Halothane - a potent inhalation anesthetic that is non-irritating, causes a concentration-dependent hypotension, and a depression of the respiratory center. Depresses neuronal transmission, causing stage III surgical anesthesia.

9. Hyperalgesia - excessive sensitivity to pain.

10. Isoflurane - a potent inhalation anesthetic that has similar action to halothane, but is less cardiodepressant.

11. L-dopa (Sinemet) - see Marieb, p. 485.

12. Maprotiline - a non-tricyclic antidepressant whose action is similar to amitriptyline, but has fewer autonomic side-effects.

13. Nitrous Oxide - used as a non-inflammable carrier gas for volatile agents since it is not potent enough to use as a sole anesthetic agent. A good analgesic in childbirth, oral surgery, and others.

14. Phenobarbital - used for generalized tonic-chronic seizures. Acts by inhibiting synaptic transmission at all levels of the CNS.

15. Phenelzine - a monoamine oxidase inhibitor, but may cause severe side effects and is rarely used. Acts to increase the reuptake of amine transmitters.

16. Phenytoin (Dilantin) - used for generalized tonic-clonic seizures. Acts by inhibiting posttetanic potentiation by membrane stabilization.

17. Transcutaneous Electrical Nerve Stimulation (TENS) - the placement of electrodes on the body surface directly over nerve fibers that transmit pain. Stimulation of the area appears to relieve pain transmission.

MATCHING QUESTIONS

Match the stages of sleep below:
a. Stage 1
b. Stage 2
c. Stage 3
d. Stage 4
e. REM

___ 1. The stage when vital signs (blood pressure, heart rate, and body temperature) reach their lowest normal levels.
___ 2. Indicated by movement of the eyes under the lids; dreaming occurs.
___ 3. Theta and delta waves begin to appear.
___ 4. Very easy to awaken; EEG shows alpha waves; may even deny being asleep.
___ 5. Typified by sleep spindles.
___ 6. Begins 90 minutes after sleep begins.
___ 7. Necessary for emotional health; may be neural "debugging."

Qtype:»Memory   Outline:»III.C.2.   Text pp.»487
Answers:»1-d; 2-e; 3-c; 4-a; 5-b; 6-e; 7-e

Match the following:
a. Alpha
b. Beta
c. Delta
d. Theta

___ 1. Typical of the alert, wide-awake state.
___ 2. Low frequency waves; uncommon in healthy awake adults.
___ 3. Seen in relaxed individuals with eyes closed.
___ 4. Typical of slow-wave deep sleep.

Qtype:»Memory   Outline:»III.B.2.   Text pp.»485-486
Answers:»1-b; 2-d; 3-a; 4-c

Match the following:
a. Programs level
b. Projection level
c. Segmental level

___ 1. The neural machinery of the spinal cord.
___ 2. Includes cortical and brain stem motor areas.
___ 3. The cerebellum and basal nuclei.

Qtype:»Memory   Outline:»II.A.   Text pp.»480-484
Answers:»1-c; 2-b; 3-a

Match the following:

a. Perceptual detection
b. Feature abstraction
c. Magnitude estimation

d. Quality discrimination
e. Pattern recognition
f. Spatial discrimination

___ 1. Term that refers to the ability of the brain to recognize stimulus strength.

___ 2. The ability that allows us to see a face when we look at a computer-generated picture made of X's.

___ 3. Recognition that stimulation has occurred.

___ 4. Identifies the site or pattern of stimulation.

___ 5. Involves the overlap and interpretation of several stimulus properties at the same time; allows recognition of substances by their texture.

___ 6. Ability to distinguish submodalities of a particular sense, e.g., sweet, sour, bitter, and salt submodalities of taste.

Qtype:»Memory   Outline:»I.B.4.   Text pp.»478-479
Answers:»1-c; 2-e; 3-a; 4-f; 5-b; 6-d

TRUE/FALSE QUESTIONS

1. The RAS appears to involve specific pathways exclusively in the limbic system.

         a. true   b. false

Qtype:»Concept   Outline:»III.C.1.b.   Text pp.»487
Answers:»false

2. Wernicke's area appears to be active in perceptual speech.

         a. true   b. false

Qtype:»Memory   Outline:»III.F.1.   Text pp.»493
Answers:»true

3. NREM sleep normally exhibits six distinct stages which appear to alternate.

         a. true   b. false

Qtype:»Concept   Outline:»III.C.2.a.   Text pp.»487
Answers:»false

4. The key center for sensorimotor integration and control and for muscle coordination is the cerebral cortex.

            a. true   b. false

Qtype:»Memory   Outline:»II.A.4.b.   Text pp.»484
Answers:»false

5. Huntingtons disease is probably a defect within the cerebellar cortex.
        a. true   b. false

Qtype:»Memory   Outline:»II.B.2.c.   Text pp.»485
Answers:»false

---

6. A brain wave pattern seen during deep sleep and during anesthesia, could be delta waves.
        a. true   b. false

Qtype:»Memory   Outline:»III.B.2.d.   Text pp.»486
Answers:»true

---

7. Alpha waves are commonly associated with cases of petit mal epilepsy.
        a. true   b. false

Qtype:»Memory   Outline:»III.B.3.b.   Text pp.»486
Answers:»false

---

8. Individuals who have the grand mal form of epilepsy frequently lose consciousness, exhibit convulsions, and experience permanent brain damage after each seizure.
        a. true   b. false

Qtype:»Concept   Outline:»III.B.3.d.   Text pp.»487
Answers:»false

---

9. Destruction of the hippocampus and amygdala regions of the brain results in widespread amnesia especially for recent facts and events.
        a. true   b. false

Qtype:»Concept   Outline:»III.E.3.a.   Text pp.»491
Answers:»true

---

10. The cerebellum appears to be involved in language use.
        a. true   b. false

Qtype:»Concept   Outline:»III.F.3.   Text pp.»493
Answers:»true

---

11. The sleep neurotransmitter is thought to be dopamine.
        a. true   b. false

Qtype:»Memory   Outline:»III.C.2.   Text pp.»488
Answers:»false

12. In order to regulate motor activity, to start and stop movements, and to coordinate postural movements, the cerebellum and basal nuclei are involved.
                    a. true   b. false

        Qtype:»Concept   Outline:»II.A.4.   Text pp.»483-484
        Answers:»true

___

13. One disorder of the substantia nigra is Parkinson's disease.
                    a. true   b. false

        Qtype:»Memory   Outline:»II.B.2.   Text pp.»485
        Answers:»true

___

14. Conscious interpretation of stimuli is called sensation.
                    a. true   b. false

        Qtype:»Memory   Outline:»I.A.   Text pp.»476
        Answers:»false

___

15. Ataxia is the coordinate activation of agonist and antagonist muscles to produce smooth well-coordinated movements.
                    a. true   b. false

        Qtype:»Concept   Outline:»II.B.1.a.   Text pp.»484
        Answers:»false

___

16. The projection level circuits that excite or inhibit a special set of spinal cord motor neurons, are called command neurons.
                    a. true   b. false

        Qtype:»Memory   Outline:»II.A.3.a.   Text pp.»483
        Answers:»true

___

17. In synthetic discrimination, each quality retains its uniqueness and is detectable individually.
                    a. true   b. false

        Qtype:»Concept   Outline:»I.B.4.f.   Text pp.»479
        Answers:»false

___

18. Every individual has his/her own pain threshold.
                    a. true   b. false

        Qtype:»Concept   Outline:»I.B.4.a.   Text pp.»481
        Answers:»false

___

19. Insomnia is involuntary lapses into sleep that occur without warning during waking hours.
    a. true   b. false

    Qtype:»Memory   Outline:»III.C.4.b.   Text pp.»489
    Answers:»false

20. The phenomenon by which visceral pain is perceived as somatic pain is called referred pain.
    a. true   b. false

    Qtype:»Memory   Outline:»I.B.4.a.   Text pp.»481
    Answers:»true

MULTIPLE-CHOICE QUESTIONS

1. Which of the following structures is probably **not** directly involved in memory?
    a. hippocampus   d. prefrontal cortex
    b. medulla   e. diencephalon
    c. amygdala

    Qtype:»Memory   Outline:»III.E.3.   Text pp.»491-492
    Answers:»b

2. According to recent research, the position at the top of the motor control heirarchy is occupied by the:
    a. spinal cord.
    b. brainstem centers.
    c. cerebellum and basal nuclei.
    d. cerebral motor cortex.

    Qtype:»Memory   Outline:»II.A.1.   Text pp.»481
    Answers:»c

3. Response to a painful stimulus is influenced by which of the following?
    a. age
    b. cultural background
    c. psychological factors
    d. physiological factors
    e. All of the above are correct.

    Qtype:»Memory   Outline:»I.B.4.   Text pp.»480-481
    Answers:»e

4. Stimuli for visceral pain include all of the following <u>except</u>:
   a. ischemia.
   b. stretching of tissue.
   c. irritating chemicals.
   d. somatic irritation.
   e. All of the above are stimuli for visceral pain.

   Qtype:»Memory   Outline:»I.B.4.   Text pp.»481
   Answers:»d

5. The nonspecific ascending pathways:
   a. are older evolutionarily.
   b. receive inputs from a few very specific types of sensory receptors.
   c. are not involved in the emotional aspects of perception.
   d. can not convey proprioceptive impulses.
   e. All of the above are correct.

   Qtype:»Concept   Outline:»I.B.3.b.   Text pp.»478
   Answers:»a

6. The pattern for walking:
   a. is regulated by CPG's.
   b. is learned.
   c. appears to involve command neurons.
   d. is controlled solely by the cerebral cortex.
   e. both a and c are correct.

   Qtype:»Concept   Outline:»II.A.2.   Text pp.»482
   Answers:»e

7. The three primary levels of neural integration in a sensory system include all but:
   a. receptor level.   c. perceptual level.
   b. circuit level.   d. effector level.

   Qtype:»Memory   Outline:»I.B.1.   Text pp.»477
   Answers:»d

8. Brain wave patterns are influenced by all the following <u>except</u>:
   a. age.
   b. sensory input.
   c. changes in composition of blood and ECF.
   d. presence of brain disease.
   e. patterns are influenced by all the above.

   Qtype:»Concept   Outline:»III.B.2.   Text pp.»486
   Answers:»e

9. An engram may actually be:
    a. modifications of myelination of neural processes.
    b. deposits of extracellular lipids and fatty acids.
    c. changes in neuronal RNA.
    d. neural activation of glial cells.
    e. All of the above are correct.

      Qtype:»Concept   Outline:»III.E.4.   Text pp.»492
      Answers:»c

10. The circuit level of the somatosensory system involves CNS centers in all of the following
    except the:
    a. spinal cord.   c. brain stem.
    b. thalamus.   d. cerebral cortex.

      Qtype:»Memory   Outline:»I.B.3.a.   Text pp.»477-478
      Answers:»d

11. The process of linking new facts with old facts already stored in in the memory bank is
    called:
    a. consolidation.   c. long term memory.
    b. automatic memory.   d. rehearsal.

      Qtype:»Memory   Outline:»III.E.1.c.   Text pp.»490
      Answers:»a

12. REM sleep is associated with:
    a. decreased vital signs.
    b. decreased activity of the brain.
    c. temporary skeletal muscle paralysis, with the exception of the extrinsic eye muscles.
    d. decreased oxygen use.

      Qtype:»Concept   Outline:»III.C.2.b.   Text pp.»487
      Answers:»c

13. Long term memory is facilitated best by:
    a. NREM sleep immediately after the event.
    b. convergent circuits.
    c. consolidation.
    d. parasympathetic activation.
    e. two of the above are correct.

      Qtype:»Concept   Outline:»III.E.1.b.   Text pp.»490
      Answers:»c

14. Important nuclei of the indirect (multineural) system that receive impulses from the equilibrium apparatus of the inner ear and help to maintain balance by varying muscle tone of postural muscles are the:
    a. red nucleus.
    b. vestibular nuclei.
    c. reticular nuclei.
    d. superior colliculi.

    Qtype:»Memory   Outline:»II.A.3.c.   Text pp.»483
    Answers:»b

15. NREM sleep in contrast to REM sleep is associatied with:
    a. increased oxygen use.
    b. rapid eye movement.
    c. sleep spindles.
    d. vital signs are reaching their highest levels.

    Qtype:»Concept   Outline:»III.C.2.a.   Text pp.»487
    Answers:»c

16. Which of the following would be the most unlikely cause of coma?
    a. a blow to the head producing cerebral edema
    b. brain stem trauma
    c. cerebral infarct
    d. drug overdose
    e. liver failure

    Qtype:»Concept   Outline:»III.D.1.   Text pp.»489
    Answers:»c

17. Cerebellar disorders may be indicated by all except:
    a. a drunken sailor gait.
    b. lack of check.
    c. decline in muscle tone.
    d. chorea.
    e. scanning speech.

    Qtype:»Memory   Outline:»II.B.1.   Text pp.»484
    Answers:»d

18. Which of the following are part of the indirect (multineural) system?
    a. vestibular nuclei
    b. red nucleus
    c. superior colliculi
    d. reticular nuclei
    e. All of the above are correct.

    Qtype:»Memory   Outline:»II.A.3.c.   Text pp.»483
    Answers:»e

19. Second order neurons of both the specific and nonspecific ascending pathways terminate in the:
    a. spinal cord.
    b. medulla.
    c. thalamus.
    d. somatosensory cortex.

    Qtype:»Memory   Outline:»I.B.3.   Text pp.»478
    Answers:»c

20. The element that does **not** belong with the other elements of the following grouping is:
    a. direct system.
    b. indirect system.
    c. projection level.
    d. CPG.
    e. command neurons.

    Qtype:»Memory   Outline:»II.A.3.   Text pp.»482
    Answers:»d

21. Skill memory is assoicated with all the following <u>except</u>:
    a. is hard to unlearn.
    b. acquired through practice.
    c. must involve the midbrain.
    d. best remembered in the doing.
    e. All of the above are correct.

    Qtype:»Concept   Outline:»III.E.2.b.   Text pp.»491
    Answers:»c

22. Processing at the circuit level involves:
        1. nonspecific ascending pathways.
        2. magnitude estimation.
        3. specific ascending pathways.
    a. 1 only
    b. 2 only
    c. 3 only
    d. 1 and 3
    e. 2 and 3

    Qtype:»Memory   Outline:»I.B.3.   Text pp.»478
    Answers:»d

23. The measurement and recording of brain wave activity can indicate:
    a. mental activity
    b. death
    c. an unconscious state.
    d. pathology of the brain.
    e. All the above are correct.

    Qtype:»Memory   Outline:»III.B.2.   Text pp.»486
    Answers:»e

24. Fact memory:
    a. is the ability to learn specific information.
    b. is best remembered in the doing.
    c. is hard to unlearn when learned once.
    d. usually involves motor skills.
    e. All of the above are correct.

   Qtype:»Memory   Outline:»III.E.2.   Text pp.»490
   Answers:»a

25. Which of the following is/are true about human memory?
    a. Memories are stored in bits and pieces all over the cerebral cortex.
    b. Parts of the limbic system help incorporate experiences into memory.
    c. The thalamus and hypothalamus are involved.
    d. Consolidation occurs
    e. All of the above are correct.

   Qtype:»Memory   Outline:»III.E.3.   Text pp.»491-492
   Answers:»e

26. Human speech involves:
    a. Wernicke's area.
    b. Broca's area.
    c. the anterior cingulate region in the midfrontal cortex.
    d. the cerebellum.
    e. All of the above are correct.

   Qtype:»Memory   Outline:»III.F.   Text pp.»493
   Answers:»d

27. Which of the following conditions is/are correct?
    a. A perception is subconscious awareness of a sensation.
    b. A sensation is consciously noticed.
    c. If one were in a very warm room, and did not "notice" the warmth until 10 minutes
       later, sensation alone existed for the first 10 minutes followed by sensation plus
       perception.
    d. Only a and b are correct
    e. A, b and c are correct.

   Qtype:»Concept   Outline:»I.A.   Text pp.»476
   Answers:»c

28. One of the most potent pain producing agents known is:
    a. histamine   d. epinephrine
    b. prostaglandin   e. norepinephrine
    c. bradykinin

   Qtype:»Memory   Outline:»I.B.4.   Text pp.»480
   Answers:»c

29. Which of the following is most correct about pain?
    a. Pain is a simple reflexive process.
    b. Bradykinin is one of the body's natural opiates, in that pain perception is greatly reduced.
    c. Interneurons in the dorsal horns releases the pain reducing substance bradykinin.
    d. Rubbing a painful area can reduce the intensity of perceived pain by causing the release of the body's natural opiates.
    e. B and c are correct.

    Qtype:»Concept   Outline:»I.B.4.   Text pp.»481
    Answers:»d

30. Select the correct definition:
    a. Magnitude estimation is the simplest level of sensation.
    b. Perceptual detection is the ability to detect how much stimulus is applied to the body.
    c. Feature abstraction allows identification of the pattern of stimulation.
    d. Spacial discrimination allows us to recognize textures.
    e. None of the above are correct.

    Qtype:»Memory   Outline:»I.B.4.b.   Text pp.»478-479
    Answers:»e

31. An electroencephalogram normally:
    a. is a record of total body electrical activity.
    b. indicates a normal frequency range of 1-30 Hz.
    c. indicates an average amplitude of 20-100 V.
    d. can not detect abnormal electrical activity.
    e. All the above are correct.

    Qtype:»Memory   Outline:»III.B.1.   Text pp.»485
    Answers:»b

SHORT-ANSWER QUESTIONS

1. Describe the main ideas of the holistic processing school of thought, relative to consciousness.

    Qtype:»Concept   Outline:»III.D.2.   Text pp.»489
    Answers:»Holistic processing involves many lines of reasoning which suppose that: (1) consciousness involves simultaneous activity of large areas of the cerebral cortex; (2) that consciousness is superimposed on other types of neural activity; and (3) that consciousness is totally interconnected.

2. Differentiate clearly between short term and long term memory.

Qtype:»Concept   Outline:»III.E.1.   Text pp.»490
Answers:»Short term memory is a fleeting memory of events that one is continuously
exposed to, and seems to be limited to 7-8 chunks of information at a time. Long term
memory is a semi-permanent storage of information that involves the transfer of data, from
STM banks to LTM banks, based on several factors such as rehersal, emotional state, and
association.

3. Describe the role of the reticular activating system in cortical arousal and stimulation.

Qtype:»Concept   Outline:»III.C.1.b.   Text pp.»487
Answers:»The reticular activating system (RAS) appears to mediate the alertness state of
the cerebral cortex. The thalamus, hypothalamus and other areas such as the brain stem
appear to be interconnedted with the RAS. Hypothalamus seems to be the structure
responsible for the actual timing of the sleep-wake cycles. The neurotransmitter serotonin
is also involved.

4. How is a receptor potential similar to an EPSP generated at a synapse?

Qtype:»Concept   Outline:»I.B.2.   Text pp.»477
Answers:»A receptor potential acts essentially the same as an EPSP in that stimulus
causes changes in permeability of the receptor membrane which results in a graded
potential. It will increase or decrease depending on the intensity of the stimulus.

CLINICAL QUESTIONS

1. Myrtle has suffered a stroke. She can understand speech and has no problem articulating
words, but her sentences do not make sense. Where is the cerebral infarct?

Qtype:»Application Outline:»III.F.1.   Text pp.»
Answers:»Probably in Wernicke's area.

2. Jessica noticed that a fellow office worker was acting very strangely. Every so often, the
fellow would slump into his chair and casually fall asleep for about 10 to 15 minutes.
Everything else seemed to be normal. What do you think the disorder would be?

Qtype:»Application Outline:»III.C.4.a.   Text pp.»488
Answers:»The worker probably has a disease called narcolepsy, a sleep disorder in which
the victim lapses involuntarily into sleep during normal waking hours. The "attacks" can
occur at any time.

3. The Ectors decided to visit a hospitalized friend who was in a serious accident which caused severe head injuries. They were told she had anterograde amnesia. What do you think they could expect?

Qtype:»Application Outline:»III.E.3.   Text pp.»492
Answers:»A person with this type of defect could carry on a conversation but could not remember what was previously discussed. Old memories are not lost but new sensory input can not be associated with the old. This person lives here and now.

16

The Special Senses

CHAPTER PREVIEW

In this chapter, the functional anatomy of each of the special sense organs, smell, taste, sight, hearing, and equilibrium will be considered. How they communicate and integrate with the central nervous system will be explored along with the homeostatic imbalances as they relate to each of these senses.

AT A GLANCE

INTEGRATING THE PACKAGE

SUGGESTED LECTURE OUTLINE

I. The Chemical Sense: Taste and Smell (pp. 496-501)
    A. Taste Buds and the Sense of Taste (pp. 496-499)
        1. Localization and Structure of Taste Buds (Fig. 16.1, p. 497)

a. Papillae
b. Taste Buds
2. Basic Taste Sensations (Fig. 16.2, p. 498)
a. Basic Qualities
b. Sensitivity
3. Activation of Taste Receptors
4. The Gustatory Pathway
a. Facial Nerve
b. Glossopharyngeal Nerve
c. Vagus Nerve
5. Influence of Other Senses on Taste
a. Smell
b. Other Senses
B. The Olfactory Epithelium and the Sense of Smell pp. 499-501)
1. Localization and Structure of Olfactory Receptors(Fig.16.3,p.500)
a. Olfactory Epithelium
b. Olfactory Nerve
2. Specificity of the Olfactory Receptors
3. Activation of Olfactory Receptors
4. Olfactory Pathway
a. Olfactory Bulbs
b. Olfactory Tracts
c. Olfactory Cortex
C. Homeostatic Imbalances of the Chemical Senses (p. 501)
1. Anosmias
2. Uncinate Fits

II. The Eye and Vision (pp. 501-521)
A. Basic Characteristics (p. 501)
B. Accessory Structures of the Eye (pp. 501-504; Fig. 16.5,p. 502)
1. Eyebrows
2. Eyelids
a. Canthi
b. Caruncle
c. Tarsal Plates
d. Eyelashes
e. Glands
3. Conjunctiva
a. Basic Features
b. Conjunctival Sacs
4. Lacrimal Apparatus
a. Lacrimal Glands
b. Lacrimal Canals (Ducts)
c. Lacrimal Sacs
d. Nasolacrimal Ducts
e. Lacrimal Secretions
5. Extrinsic Eye Muscles (Fig. 16.6, p. 504)
a. Annular Ring
b. Rectus Muscles
c. Oblique Muscles
d. Neural Control
C. Structure of the Eye (pp. 505-509; Fig. 16.7, p. 505)
1. Tunics Forming the Wall of the Eye
a. Fibrous Tunic

1. Sclera
2. Cornea
b. Vascular Tunic
1. Choroid
2. Ciliary body
3. Iris
4. Pupil
c. Sensory Tunic
1. Pigmented Layer
2. Neural Layer (Fig. 16.9, p. 507)
3. Optic Disc (Fig. 16.10, p. 508)
4. Photoreceptors
5. Macula Lutea
6. Fovea Centralis
2. Internal Chambers and Fluids (Fig. 16.11, p. 508)
a. Posterior Cavity
1. Vitreous Humor
2. Functions of Humor
b. Anterior Cavity
1. Anterior Chamber
2. Posterior Chamber
3. Aqueous Humor
4. Functions of Humor
5. Canal of Schlemm
6. Glaucoma
3. Lens
a. Basic Features
b. Lens Epithelium
c. Lens Fibers
d. Cataracts
D. Physiology of Vision (pp. 509-521)
1. Overview: Light and Optics
a. Wavelength and Color (Fig. 16.12, p. 510)
b. Refraction and Lenses (Figs. 16.13 and 16.14,pp. 510-511)
2. Focusing of Light on the Retina
a. Basic Features
b. Focusing for Distance Vision (Fig. 16.15, p. 511)
c. Focusing for Close Vision
1. Accomodation of the Lens
2. Constriction of the Pupils
3. Convergence of the Eyeballs
d. Homeostatic Imbalances of Refraction (Fig. 16.16,p. 513)
3. Photoreception
a. Functional Anatomy of the Photoreceptors (Fig. 16.17, p. 514)
1. Outer Segment
2. Inner Segment
b. The Chemistry of Visual Pigments
1. Retinene
2. Retinal Isomers
4. Stimulation of the Photoreceptors
a. Excitation of Rods
1. Rhodopsin
2. Scotopsin
3. Bleaching

b. Excitation of Cones
  1. Photopsins
c. Light and Dark Adaptation
5. The Visual Pathway to the Brain (Fig. 16.21, p. 519)
  a. Neural Pathways
  b. Optic Chiasm
  c. Optic Nerves
  d. Neural Centers
6. Binocular Vision and Stereopsis
  a. Binocular Vision
  b. Depth Perception
  c. Three-Dimentional Vision
  d. Homeostatic Disorders
7. Visual Processing
  a. Retinal Processing
    1. On-Center Fields
    2. Off-Center Fields
    3. Center-Surround Antagonism
  b. Thalamic Processing
  c. Cortical Processing
    1. Simple Cortical Neurons
    2. Complex Cortical Neurons

III. The Ear: Hearing and Balance (pp. 521-533)

  A. Structure of the Ear (pp. 521-525; Fig. 16.24, p. 522)
    1. The Outer Ear
      a. Auricle (Pinna)
      b. External Auditory Canal
        1. Ceruminous Glands
        2. Tympanic Membrane
    2. The Middle Ear
      a. Oval Window
      b. Round Window
      c. Epitympanic Recess
      d. Mastoid Antrum
      e. Auditory (Eustachian) Tube
      f. Ear Ossicles
        1. Malleus (Hammer)
        2. Incus (Anvil)
        3. Stapes (Stirrup)
      g. Tensor Tympani
      h. Stapedius Muscle
      i. Tympanic Reflex
    3. The Inner Ear
      a. Labyrinth (Fig. 16.25, p. 523)
        1. Bony Labyrinth
        2. Membranous Labyrinth
        3. Perilymph
        4. Endolymph
      b. The Vestibule
        1. Saccule
        2. Utricle
      c. The Semicircular Canals
        1. Semicircular Ducts

   2. Ampulla
   3. Crista Ampullaris
  d. The Cochlea (Fig. 16.26, p. 524)
   1. Modiolus
   2. Cochlear Duct
   3. Organ of Corti and Spiral Lamina
   4. Scala Vestibuli
   5. Scala Media
   6. Scala Tympani
   7. Helicotrema
   8. Vestibular Membrane
   9. Basilar Membrane
B. Sound and Mechanisms of Hearing (pp. 525-529)
 1. Properties of Sound
  a. Basic Features (Fig. 16.27, p. 525)
  b. Frequency (Fig. 16.28, p. 526)
  c. Amplitude
 2. Transmission of Sound to the Inner Ear
 3. Resonance of the Basilar Membrane (Fig. 16.29, p. 527)
 4. Excitation of Hair Cells in the Organ of Corti
  a. Organ of Corti
  b. Cochlear Hair Cells
  c. Tectorial Membrane
 5. Auditory Pathway to the Brain (Fig. 16.30, p. 528)
 6. Auditory Processing
  a. Perception of Pitch
  b. Detection of Loudness
  c. Localization of Sound
C. Homeostatic Imbalances of Hearing (pp. 529-530)
 1. Deafness
  a. Conduction Deafness
  b. Sensineural Deafness
 2. Tinnitus
 3. Meniere's Syndrome
D. Mechanisms of Equilibrium and Orientation (pp. 530-533)
 1. Basic Features
 2. Function of the Maculae in Static Equilibrium (Fig.16.31, p.530)
  a. Maculae
   1. Supporting Cells
   2. Hair Cells
  b. Otolithic Membrane
   1. Otoliths
  c. Vestibular Nerve
  d. Mechanism of Action
 3. Function of the Crista Ampullaris in Dynamic Equilibrium (Fig. 16.32, p. 532)
  a. Crista Ampullaris
  b. Cupula
  c. Mechanism of Action
  d. Vestibular Nystagmus
 4. The Equilibrium Pathway to the Brain (Fig. 16.33, p. 533)
  a. Vestibular Nuclear Complex
  b. Cerebellum
  c. Homeostatic Imbalances

IV. Developmental Aspects of the Special Senses (pp. 534-536)
   A. Embryonic and Fetal Development of the Senses (p. 534, Fig. 16.34, p. 535)
   B. Development of the Senses Through Adolescence (p. 534)
   C. Effect of Aging on the Senses (p. 534)

REVIEW ITEMS

1. Epithelia, (Chapter 4, pp. 104-113)

2. Exocrine glands, (Chapter 4, pp. 112-113)

3. Connective tissues, (Chapter 4, pp. 114-126)

4. Sebaceous glands, (Chapter 5, p. 148)

5. Sudoriferous glands, (Chapter 5, p. 147)

6. Synovial joints, (Chapter 8, pp. 226-239)

7. Skeletel muscle naming, (Chapter 10, pp. 288-290)

8. Chemoreceptors, (Chapter 13, p. 424)

9. Synapses, (Chapter 11, pp. 360-362)

10. Neurotransmitters, (Chapter 11, pp. 365-370)

11. Cerebral cortex, (Chapter 12, pp. 383-392)

12. Thalamus, (Chapter 12, p. 392)

13. Receptor and generator potentials, (Chapter 13, p. 425)

14. Cranial Nerves, (Chapter 13, pp. 430-438)

15. Reflex activity, (Chapter 13, op. 447-453)

CROSS-REFERENCES

1. Formation of the aqueous humor is similar to CSF formation described in Chapter 12, p. 404.

2. Inflammation is described in detail in Chapter 22, pp. 692-695).

3. Secretion of saliva (p. 778) and gastric juice (pp. 788) is described in detail in Chapter 24.

4. The salivary reflex is presented in Chapter 24, p. 779.

5. Papillae and taste buds are further explained in Chapter 24, pp. 776-777.

6. The relationship between the auditory tube and the respiratory system is described in Chapter 23, p. 728.

ANSWERS TO TEXTBOOK CHAPTER QUESTIONS

Multiple Choice/Matching

1. d	14. a
2. a	15. b
3. d	16. b
4. c	17. b
5. d	18. d
6. b	19. b
7. c	20. c
8. d	21. d
9. a	22. b
10. b	23. b
11. c	24. e
12. d	25. b
13. b	26. c

Short Answer Essay Questions

27. Sweet - anterior portion of the tongue; salty - anterior portion and lateral edges of the tongue; sour - lateral edges of the tongue; bitter - posterior-most portion of the tongue. The sensation for sweet substances overlaps sour and salty areas. (p. 498)

28. The receptors are located in the roof of each nasal cavity. The site is poorly suited because air entering the nasal cavities must make a hairpin turn to stimulate the receptors. (p. 499)

29. The nasolacrimal duct empties into the nasal cavity. (p. 503).

30. Rods are dim-light visual receptors, while cones are for bright-light and high-acuity color vision. (pp. 513-514)

31. The fovea contains only cones and provides detailed color vision for critical vision. (p. 515)

32. Retinal changes to the all-trans form; the retinal-scotopsin combination breaks down, separating retinal and scotopsin (bleaching) in the sequence: prelumirhodopsin --> lumirhodopsin --> metarhodopsin I --> metarhodopsin II --> pararhodopsin. The net effect is to "turn off" sodium entry into the cell effectively hyperpolarizing the rod. (p. 516)

33. Each cone responds maximally to one of these colors of light, but there is overlap in their absorption spectra that accounts for the other hues. (p. 516; Fig. 16.20, p. 517)

34. With age, the lens loses its crystal clarity and becomes discolored, and the dilator muscles become less efficient. Atrophy of the organ of Corti reduces hearing acuity, especially for high-pitch sounds. The sense of smell and taste diminishes due to a gradual loss of receptors, thus their appetite is diminished. (p. 536)

Critical Thinking and Application Questions

1. Papilledema - a nipplelike protrusion of the optic disc into the eyeball, which is caused by conditions that increase intracranial pressure. A rise in cerebrospinal fluid pressure caused by an intracranial tumor will compress the walls of the central vein resulting in its congestion and bulging of the optic disc. (p. 536)

2. Pathogenic microoogranisms spread from the nasopharynx through the auditory tube into the tympanic cavity. They may then spread posteriorly into the mastoid air cells via the mastoid antrum resulting in mastoiditis. They may then extend medially to the inner ear causing secondary labyrinthitis. If unchecked, the infection may spread to the meninges causing meningitis and possibly an abscess in the temporal lobe of the brain or in the cerebellum. They may also enter into the blood causing septicemia. The cause of her dizziness and loss of balance is a disruption of the equilibrium apparatus due to the infectious process. (pp. 523-524)

3. Conjunctivitis. The foreign object probably would be found in the conjunctival sac near the orifice of the lacrimal canals. (p. 503)

4. This is known as a detached retina. The condition is serious, but it can be reattached surgically using lasers before permanent damage occurs. (p. 508)

5. The inability to hear high pitched sounds is called presbycusis, a type of sensineural deafness. It is caused by the gradual loss of hearing receptors throughout life, but is accelerated if one is exposed to loud rock music for extended periods. (p. 536)

LABORATORY CORRELATIONS

1. Marieb, E. N. Human Anatomy and Physiology Laboratory Manual: Cat and Fetal Pig Versions. 3rd. ed. Benjamin/Cummings, 1989.

    Exercise 24: Special Senses: Vision
    Exercise 25: Special Senses: Hearing and Equilibrium
    Exercise 26: Special Senses: Taste and Olfaction

2. Marieb, E. N. Human Anatomy and Physiology Laboratory Manual: Brief Version. 3rd. ed. Benjamin/Cummings, 1992.

    Exercise 21: Special Senses: Vision
    Exercise 22: Special Senses: Hearing and Equilibrium
    Exercise 23: Special Senses: Taste and Olfaction

OVERHEAD TRANSPARENCIES INDEX

Transparency	Description
16.1	Location and structure of taste buds
16.3	Olfactory receptors
16.5	Accessory structures of the eye
16.6a/b	Extrinsic muscles of the eyes
16.7	Interior structure of the eye (sagittal section)
16.9	Schematic view of the retina
16.11	Structures of the anterior portion of the eye
16.17a	Rods and cones of the retina
16.24	Structure of the ear
16.26	Anatomy of the cochlea

BASSETT ATLAS SLIDES AND FIGURES INDEX

Slide #	Figure	Description
5	1.5A,B	Base of the Brain
6	1.6	Circle of Willis
8	1.8A,B	Sagittal section of the brain
16	2.5A,B	Eye

BLACK LINE MASTER INDEX

Black Line Master	Description
16.3	Olfactory receptors
16.5	Accessory structures of the eye
16.6a/b	Extrinsic muscles of the eyes

INSTRUCTIONAL AIDS

LECTURE HINTS

1. Emphasize that each taste sensation is not localized to a specific area, but that there is significant overlap of the different sensation areas. Students often assume that a particular point on the tongue responds to a single type of substance.

2. Point out the importance of other sensations (especially smell) on the perception of taste.

3. During the lecture on olfactory anatomy, ask the class what would happen to olfaction if mucus glands below the olfactory epithelium were absent.

4. Emphasize that olfactory receptors are the only renewable neurons in the body and are therefore the one exception to the rule that neurons do not replicate.

5. Point out that special sense receptor cells develop potential just like neurons (sodium and potassium gradients) do, and that even with all the apparent complexity of the body, often slight modifications to a single basic blueprint is all that is necessary to achieve a totally new function.

6. There is often confusion in the terminology of the chambers of the eye. Point out that the anterior segment is divided into anterior and posterior chambers by the iris.

7. Initially, it is difficult for even the best students to grasp the concept of ciliary muscle contraction leading to lens thickening (for close focus). Intuitively, most think of the process of stretching the lens as a consequence of muscle contraction, not relaxation. Spend some time reinforcing this concept.

8. Have students try out focusing on objects at night. Explain that they should not look directly at the object, but slightly to one side, and the object should appear brighter. Relate this exercise to the distribution of rods and cones in the eye.

9. As a point of interest, mention that the ossicles are joined by the smallest synovial joints in the body.

10. Emphasize the difference between static and dynamic equilibrium by comparing and contrasting anatomy of each type of equilibrium.

DEMONSTRATIONS/ACTIVITIES

1. Film(s) or other audiovisual materials of choice.

2. Obtain a 3-D model of an eye and ear to illustrate the various anatomical parts of each.

3. Use an onion, orange, and apple to test the interaction of taste, smell, and sight. Have two volunteers first taste and smell each item normally. Then cover their eyes and have them taste each. Then pinch shut their noses and taste each.

4. Select four volunteers and spray a different strong cologne on their wrists. Then determine how long it takes for each to "adapt" to the cologne.

5. Dissect a fresh (or preserved if fresh is not available) beef eye to illustrate the anatomical structure and nature of the tissues and fluids.

6. Obtain a skull to illustrate the locations of any bony structures associated with our senses.

7. Obtain a set of ear ossicles to illustrate how tiny they are.

8. Bring a convex lens to class and have students hold the glass up and focus on a distant object. They will notice that it is upside down and reversed. Then explain that the human eye is also a single lens system. The question should arise: "Why don't we see things upside down?"

CRITICAL THINKING/DISCUSSION TOPICS

1. Most people with sinus infections can't smell or taste. Why?

2. Wine tasting can be a real "art." Why are some people more adept at tasting than others? What effect does smoking, alcohol, and/or sweets have on wine tasting? Why is it useful to swirl a glass of wine and then sniff it?

3. Amplified "rock music" has long been implicated in auditory deafness. What suggestions could be made to alleviate this problem in teenagers?

4. Fish and other animals have eyes on the sides of their heads. Why is this useful? Why do birds of prey, cats, and other animals have both eyes fucused on the same object (binocular vision)? Why is this useful? In a few cases, genetically-deformed children are born with eyes on the lateral sides of their heads. How could this happen and what could this suggest embryologically?

5. Certain types of sunglasses can cause more harm than good. What could be wrong with these inexpensive, designer sunglasses?

6. What would happen to gustatory and olfactory sensations if the receptors for taste and smell were specific to a single substance?

7. Since the sclera is avascular, why do we see blood vessels in the white of the eye?

8. How is it possible that the cornea is transparent and the sclera is opaque when they are both constructed of the same material, and continuous with each other?

9. Examine the consequences to the anatomy of the eye and vision if aqueous humor drainage exceeded production.

10. Explain why depth perception is lost if one eye is not functioning.

11. If the number of cones feeding into a single ganglion cell was increased ten-fold, what would be the consequence to color visual acuity?

12. Examine the consequences to sound perception if the tympanic membrane increased two-fold in surface area. What would happen if the oval window had increased surface area? Would sounds be perceived if the round window became rigid?

LIBRARY RESEARCH TOPICS

1. How successful are cochlear implants? What surgical techniques are employed?

2. Some permanently deaf individuals have been helped by means of computers and electrical probes connected to certain areas of the brain. How is this possible and what is the current research in this area?

3. Contact lens have long been used to correct vision problems. What is the status of contact lens implants and why is there a hesitance by ophthalmologists to use them?

4. What substances are found in wines such as cabernet, chardonnay, chenin blanc, and others that provide the tremendous variety of tastes and smells?

5. If hearts, lungs, and livers can be transplanted, why not eyes? What would be some of the technical difficulties?

AUDIO VISUAL AIDS/COMPUTER SOFTWARE

Films

1. The Human Eye (IFB, 14 min., C, 1978) Presents a comparison of the human eye with other animals.

2. Colors and How We See them (AF, 22 min., C, 1977) Shows how and why rods and cones of the retina relay their specific messages to the brain.

3. The Ears and Hearing (EBF, 22 min., C, 1969) Anatomy and physiology of hearing. Describes how hearing aids or surgery may help conduction deafness.

4. The Eyes and Seeing (EBF, 20 min., C, 1967) Provides a step-by-step investigation of how the eye works.

5. Hearing-Auditory System (KB, 11 min., C) Part of "Anatomical Basis of Brain Function Series."

6. The Incredible Seeing Machine (BL, 26 min., C, 1974) A class of college students explores vision, discovering how the eye works, why optical illusions occur, and how corrective lenses work.

7. Sight-Visual System (AVC, 18 min., C) A professional film on the visual system of the eye.

8. The Structure of the Eye (CCM, 7 min., C, 1970) Through eyeball dissection and animation, the anatomy and function of the eye are described.

Filmstrips/Slides

1. The Special Senses-Unit 6 (CA, RB-369, Filmstrip)

2. Sensory System in the Human Body (CA, HE0562, Filmstrip) Program illustrates eyes and ears as pathways for vision and hearing and other senses.

3. Histology of the Sensory System (EI, 614, Slides) Illustrates structural and functional correlations of a variety of sensory tissue, including the eye and ear.

4. Eyes and Their Function (EI, SS-0870F, Filmstrip or Slides) Functional description of the eyeball and accessory structures.

5. Ears and Their Function (EI, SS-0330F, Filmstrip or Slides) Studies middle and inner ear.

Videotapes

1. Eyes and Ears (FHS, QB-823, 26 min., C, VHS/BETA) Fascinating camera action used to show functions of the eye and ear. Also available in 16 mm.

2. Anatomy of the Human Eye Series (TF, C, 1987) A series of seven videotapes (or 16 mm-films), ranging from 13 to 19 minutes, explaining the gross anatomy of the human eye.

3. Optics of the Human Eye Series (TF, C, 1987) A series of four videotapes (or 16 mm-films), each ten minutes long, which illustrate basic optics relating to the eye.

4. Dissection and Anatomy of the Beef Eye (CBS, 49-2300, VHS)

Computer Software

1. Dynamics of the Human Eye (EI, C-3060, Apple or IBM)

2. Dynamics of the Human Ear (EI, C-3061, Apple or IBM)

3. Dynamics of the Human Senses of Touch, Taste, and Smell (EI, C-3063, Apple or IBM)

4. Senses: Physiology of Human Perception (PLP, CH184006, Apple II, CH184007 IBM, CH184008 MAC)

5. The Eye (QUE, COM4210A, Apple)

See *Guide to Audiovisual Resources* at the end of this module for key to AV distributors

LECTURE ENHANCEMENT MATERIAL

CLINICAL AND RELATED TERMS

1. Achromatopsia - total color blindness.

2. Ageusia - lack or impairment of the sense of taste.

3. Amblyopia - dimness of vision.

4. Ametropia - a defect in the refractive powers of the eye where images cannot be brought into proper focus on the retina.

5. Anisopia - an inequality of vision in the two eyes.

6. Astereognosis - an inability to recognize familiar objects by feeling their shape.

7. Audiometer - a device used to determine the degree of hearing impairment.

8. Blepharectomy - the surgical excision of a lesion of the eyelids.

9. Cochlear Implant - a surgical technique involving the implantation of an artificial device into the cochlea that receives impulses from an external receiver that in turn transforms the signals to the vestibulocochlear nerve resulting in rudimentary sound perception.

10. Esotropia - strabismus in which there is a deviation of the visual axis of one eye towards the other, resulting in diplopia.

11. Eustachitis - infection or inflammation of the eustachian tube.

12. Iridectomy - excision of the iris.

13. Iritis - infection or inflammation of the iris of the eye.

14. Keratitis - infection or inflammation of the cornea of the eye.

15. Kinesthesis - the sense by which weight, position, and movement are perceived.

16. Labyrinthectomy - the excision of the labyrinth of the ear.

17. Myringitis - inflammation or infection of the eardrum.

18. Ophthalmoscope - an instrument used for the examination of the interior of the eye.

19. Osmesis - the act of smelling.

20. Otoscope - an instrument used for the examination of the external auditory meatus and middle ear.

21. Ptosis - the paralytic drooping of the upper eyelid.

22. Radial Keratotomy - a surgical technique designed to improve myopia by making small incisions in the cornea, allowing it to stretch and become flatter.

23. Rhinne Tests - the use of a vibrating tuning fork held against the bone behind the ear to diagnose conductive deafness.

24. Sclerostomy - the creation of a fistula through the sclera for the relief of glaucoma.

25. Snellen Chart - a chart printed with varying size letters used in testing visual acuity.

26. Tonometry - the measurement of tension or pressure, especially intraocular pressure of the eye.

27. Uveitis - inflammation or infection of the uvea that includes the iris, ciliary body, and choroid.

28. Vertigo - dizziness, especially due to heights.

29. Weber Test - the use of a vibrating tuning fork pressed against the forehead to diagnose conductive deafness.

DISORDERS/HOMEOSTATIC IMBALANCES

Infectious Disorders

1. Congenital Rubella Syndrome - a complication occurring in the unborn fetus due to a rubella infection in the mother, usually during the first two to three months of gestation. Common fetal anomalies include cataracts, heart defects and others.

2. Mastoiditis - an inflammation of the air cells of the mastoid process. Condition is characterized by fever, chills, tenderness, and leukocytosis. May cause perisinus abscesses, periphlebitis, and lateral sinus thrombosis.

3. Ophthalmia Neonatorum - a severe purulent conjunctivitis of the eyes of newborns, usually caused by infection from Neisseria gonorrhea as the infant passes through an infected birth canal. May be prevented by applying a 1% silver nitrate solution or antibiotic ointment to the eyes shortly after birth.

4. Trachoma - a chronic, highly-contagious form of conjunctivitis caused by Chlamydia trachomatis. The disease is characterized by hypertrophy of the conjunctiva, formation of granulation tissue, and subsequent scar formation. If untreated, could cause blindness.

Disorders of the Eye

1. Chorioretinitis - an inflammation of the choroid layer and the retina.

2. Cyclopia - a developmental anomaly characterized by a single eye.

3. Nyctalopia - night blindness, usually caused by a deficiency of vitamin A.

4. Retinitis Pigmentosa - a chronic progressive disease that begins in early childhood, characterized by degeneration of the retinal epithelium, especially the rods; atrophy of the optic nerve; and extensive pigment changes in the retina.

5. Retinoblastoma - a tumor that arises from retinal blast cells. Also known as a retinal glioma. Usually occurs in young children and tends to show a hereditary pattern.

6. Sty - an inflammation of the sebaceous glands of the eyelids. Also called hordeolum.

7. Xerophthalmus - abnormally dry eyes, usually caused by a deficiency of vitamin A.

Disorders of the Ear

1. Eustachitis - infection or inflammation of the eustachian tube.

2. Macrotia - abnormally large ears.

3. Otopyorrhea - discharge of pus from the ear.

4. Tympanosclerosis - hardening of the tympanic membrane.

APPLIED PHARMACOLOGY

Mydriatics and Cycloplegics

1. Phenylephrine (Contac, Co-Tylenol, Neo-Synephrine) - used in the temporary relief of nasal and sinus congestion; contracts blood vessel walls of the nose, sinus, and throat tissues, enlarging airways. Also used in pupillary dilation.

2. Scopolamine (Donnatal, Omnibel) - used to prevent motion sickness. Blocks nerve impulses at parasympathetic nerve endings. Also used to prevent posterior fibrous adhesions on the iris.

Drugs Used for Glaucoma

1. Methazolamide (Neptazane) - similar to timolol. Acts by inhibiting carbonic anhydrase.

2. Pilocarpine HC1 (Almocarpine, Piloptic) - used in the treatment for glaucoma by reducing internal eye pressure.

3. Timolol Maleate (Timoptic) - used in the treatment of chronic open angle glaucoma by reducing aqueous humor formation.

Antimicrobial Agents

1. Bacitracin - an antibacterial agent produced by Bacillus subtilis, used topically or given intramuscularly, effective against gram-positive organisms.

2. Gentamicin - an antibiotic produced by the fungus, Micromonospora, that is effective against gram-negative bacteria, especially Pseudomonas.

3. Silver Nitrate - colorless crystals used as a caustic and local anti-infective agent. A 1% ointment is used to prevent ophthalmia neonatorum.

4. Vidarabine - a purine analog that is used as an antiviral agent to treat herpes keratitis and encephalitis. Inhibits DNA synthesis.

Anti-inflammatory Agents

1. Hydrocortisone - a glucocorticoid that inhibits edema, capillary dilation, phagocytic migration and fibrin deposition in acute inflammation. Most useful in dermatitis of the eyelids.

Agents for Dry Eyes and Decongestants

1. Methylcellulose (Murocel, Cologel) - acts as a demulcent.

2. Tetrahydrozoline HC1 (Visine, Murine) - used for topical ocular vasoconstriction by exerting a local adrenergic mechanism on conjunctival blood vessels.

Topical Anesthetic Agents

1. Proparacaine (Ophthaine) - rapidly-acting, topical anesthetic for use in removing foreign bodies from the ocular surface of the eye and for other procedures.

Otic Agents

1. Antipyrine 5.4%, Benzocaine 1.4% (Auralgan Otic) - used as an anesthetic in the treatment of painful external otitis or otitis media. May be used with antibiotics.

2. Cresylacetate (Cresylate Otic) - antifungal agent in the treatment of otomycosis.

3. Polymyxin B, Hydrocortisone (Pyrocidin-Otic) - used as an antibacterial, anti-inflammatory agent in external otitis. Depending on infectious agents, other antibiotics, such as neomycin or colistin, may be used.

SUGGESTED READINGS

1. Abu-Mostafa, Y.S., and D. Psaltis. "Optical Neural Computers." Scientific American 256 (Mar. 1987):88-96.

2. Barlow, Jr., R.B. "What the Brain Tells the Eye." Scientific American 262 (Apr. 1990):90-95.

3. Brou, P., et al., "The Color of Things." Scientific American 255 (Sept. 1986).

4. Cain, W.S. "To Know With the Nose: Keys to Odor Identifi- cation." Science 203 (1979):467.

5. Daw, N.W. "Neurophysiology of Color Vision." Physiological Reviews 53 (1973:571.

6. Durrant, J.D., and J.H. Lovrinic. Basics of Hearing Science (Baltimore:Williams and Wilkins, 1988).

7. Engen, T. "Remembering Odors and Their Names." American Scientist 75 (Sept.-Oct. 1987).

8. Fackelmann, K.A. "Smokers Suffer from Impaired Smell." Science News 137 (Mar. 1990)

9. Franklin D. "Crafting Sound From Silence." Science News 126 (Oct. 1984).

10. Gibbons, B. "The Intimate Sense." National Geographic 170 (Sept. 1986):324-360.

11. Glickstein, M. "The Discovery of the Visual Cortex." Scientific American 295 (Sept. 1988):118-127.

12. Gourse, L. "Patchwork Medicine." Science 85 (Oct. 1985):79, 81.

13. Grady, D. "Sounds Instead of Silence." Discover 4 (Oct. 1983).

14. Greenberg, J. "Early Hearing Loss and Brain Development." Science News 131 (Mar. 1987):149.

15. Hubel, D.H. and T.N. Wiesel "Brain Mechanisms of Vision." Scientific American 241 (Sept. 1979):150-162.

16. Hudspeth, A.J. "The Hair Cells of the Inner Ear." Scientific American (Jan. 1983).

17. Koretz, J.F., and G.H. Handelman. "How the Human Eye Focuses." Scientific American 259 (July 1988):92-99).

14. Loeb, G.E. "The Functional Replacement of the Ear." Scientific American (Feb. 1985).

18. Melamed, M.A. "Cataracts: Recognition and Assessment." Hospital Medicine (July 1982).

19. O'Brien, D.F. "The Chemistry of Vision." Science 218 (1982).

20. Parker, D.E. "The Vestibular Apparatus." Scientific American 243 (Nov. 1980).

21. Ramachandran, V.S., and S.M. Anstis. "The Perception of Apparent Motion." Scientific American 254 (June 1986).

22. Ross, P.E. "Smelling Better." Scientific American 262 (Mar. 1990):32.

23. Rushton, W.A. "Visual Pigments and Color Blindness." Scientific American (Mar. 1975).

24. Schnapf, J.L., and D.A. Baylor. "How Photoreceptor Cells Respond to Light." Scientific American 256 (Apr. 1987):40-47.

25. Stone, J. "Scents and Sensibility." Discover 10 (Dec. 1989):26-31.

26. Weiss, R. "Transplanting the Light Fantastic." Science News 136 (Nov. 1989):297, 300.

27. Weiss, R.L. "Eye Diving." Science News 138 (Sept. 1990):170-172.

28. Wickelgren, I. "Vitamins C and E May Prevent Cataracts." Science News 135 (May 1989):308.

29. Wolfe, J.M. "Hidden Visual Processes." Scientific American (Feb. 1983).

30. Wurtz, R.H., et al. "Brain Mechanisms of Visual Attention." Scientific American (June 1982).

HANDOUTS

The following section contains prepared handout material which may be photocopied and distributed to the class. All materials are organized so that selected items can be cut and pasted for the instructors individual needs.

If budgets are a limiting factor in the use of handouts, these masters may be placed on reserve in the library for students to photocopy at their convenience.

Preview Of Selected Key Terms

Special senses . . . . The senses of taste, smell, vosion, hearing, and equilibrium.

Taste buds . . . . Sensory receptor organs that house gustatory cells, which respond to disolved food chemicals.

Olfactory epithelium . . . . (olfact=to smell) Sensory receptor region in the nasal cavity containing olfactory neurons that respond to volatile chemicals that enter the nasal passages in air.

Extrinsis eye muscles . . . .(extrins=from the outside) The six skeletal muscles that are attached to and move each eyeball.

Sclera . . . . (scler=hard) The outer fibrous tunic of the eyeball.

Choroid . . . . (choroid=membranelike) The vascular middle tunic of the eyeball.

Retina . . . . (retin=a net) The neural tunic of the eyeball; contains photoreceptors, the rods and cones.

Accommodation . . . . Focusing for near vision.

Labyrinth . . . .(labyrinth=maze) The bony cavities and membranes of the inner ear.

Cochlea . . . . (cochlea=snail) The snail shaped chamber of the bony labyrinth that houses the receptor for hearing (Organ of Corti).

Static equilibrium . . . . The sense of head position in space with respect to gravity.

Dynamic equilibrium . . . . .The sense that reports on angular or rotatory movements of the head in space.

Macula . . . .(macula=spot) Sensory receptor organ within the vestibule of the inner ear; static equilibrium receptor.

Crista ampularis . . . . (crista=crest; ampulla=flask) Sensory receptor organ within a semicircular canal of the inner ear; dynamic equilibrium receptor.

Terms/Disorders

1. Cochlear Implant - a surgical technique involving the implantation of an artificial device into the cochlea that receives impulses from an external receiver that in turn transforms the signals to the vestibulocochlear nerve resulting in rudimentary sound perception.

2. Congenital Rubella Syndrome - a complication occurring in the unborn fetus due to a rubella infection in the mother, usually during the first two to three months of gestation. Common fetal anomalies include cataracts, heart defects and others.

3. Eustachitis - infection or inflammation of the eustachian tube.

4. Hydrocortisone - a glucocorticoid that inhibits edema, capillary dilation, phagocytic migration and fibrin deposition in acute inflammation. Most useful in dermatitis of the eyelids.

5. Mastoiditis - an inflammation of the air cells of the mastoid process. Condition is characterized by fever, chills, tenderness, and leukocytosis. May cause perisinus abscesses, periphlebitis, and lateral sinus thrombosis.

6. Ophthalmoscope - an instrument used for the examination of the interior of the eye.

7. Otoscope - an instrument used for the examination of the external auditory meatus and middle ear.

8. Phenylephrine (Contac, Co-Tylenol, Neo-Synephrine) - used in the temporary relief of nasal and sinus congestion; contracts blood vessel walls of the nose, sinus, and throat tissues, enlarging airways. Also used in pupillary dilation.

9. Radial Keratotomy - a surgical technique designed to improve myopia by making small incisions in the cornea, allowing it to stretch and become flatter.

10. Retinitis Pigmentosa - a chronic progressive disease that begins in early childhood, characterized by degeneration of the retinal epithelium, especially the rods; atrophy of the optic nerve; and extensive pigment changes in the retina.

11. Rhinne Tests - the use of a vibrating tuning fork held against the bone behind the ear to diagnose conductive deafness.

12. Scopolamine (Donnatal, Omnibel) - used to prevent motion sickness. Blocks nerve impulses at parasympathetic nerve endings. Also used to prevent posterior fibrous adhesions on the iris.

13. Snellen Chart - a chart printed with varying size letters used in testing visual acuity.

14. Tetrahydrozoline HC1 (Visine, Murine) - used for topical ocular vasoconstriction by exerting a local adrenergic mechanism on conjunctival blood vessels.

15. Tonometry - the measurement of tension or pressure, especially intraocular pressure of the eye.

16. Trachoma - a chronic, highly-contagious form of conjunctivitis caused by Chlamydia trachomatis. The disease is characterized by hypertrophy of the conjunctiva, formation of granulation tissue, and subsequent scar formation. If untreated, could cause blindness.

17. Weber Test - the use of a vibrating tuning fork pressed against the forehead to diagnose conductive deafness.

Age Associated Changes

Gustation and Olfaction

-Women have a more acute sense of smell than men
-Nonsmokers have a keener sense of smell than smokers
-The ability to taste and smell begins in the fourth decade of life
-receptors for taste and smell are gradually lost and replaced more slowly as we age
-Almost half of individuals over the age of 80 years cannot smell at all

Vision

-Lens loses transparency and becomes discolored
-Muscles of the iris become less efficient resulting in a partially constricted pupil
-By age 70 visual acuity is significantly reduced
-Incidence of cataracts, glaucoma, and other eye disorders increases

Hearing

-By age 60, significant deterioration of the spiral organ
-The ability to perceive high-pitched sounds is lost first
-Increased incidence of otosclerosis

The following section contains selected unlabeled line art representations of key elements in this chapter. These diagrams may be utilized in several ways depending on individual needs:

1. Photocopy directly onto acetate film for overhead projection during class lecture/discussion. The art is unlabeled so that the instructor may write directly on the acetate during class and emphasize critical features. A key advantage in the use of this form of visual presentation is the ease with which students are able to comprehend complex anatomical and physiological relationships presented during class.

2. Photocopy for handouts so that the students may take notes directly on the diagrams and in that way have a clear understanding of the relationship between the figure and lecture material.

3. If the course is on a tight budget, place masters of diagrams on reserve (usually in a notebook in the library) for students to make copies should they choose to do so.

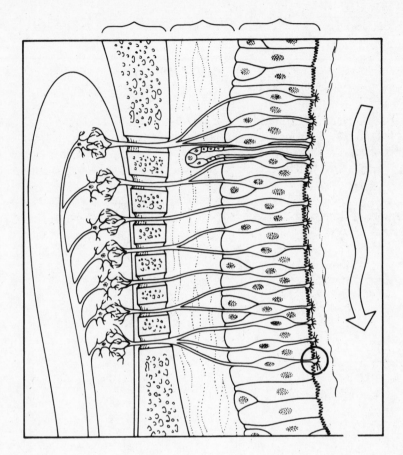

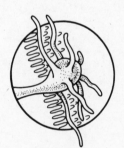

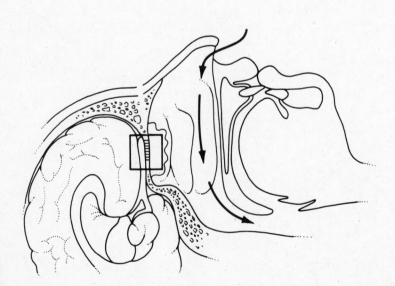

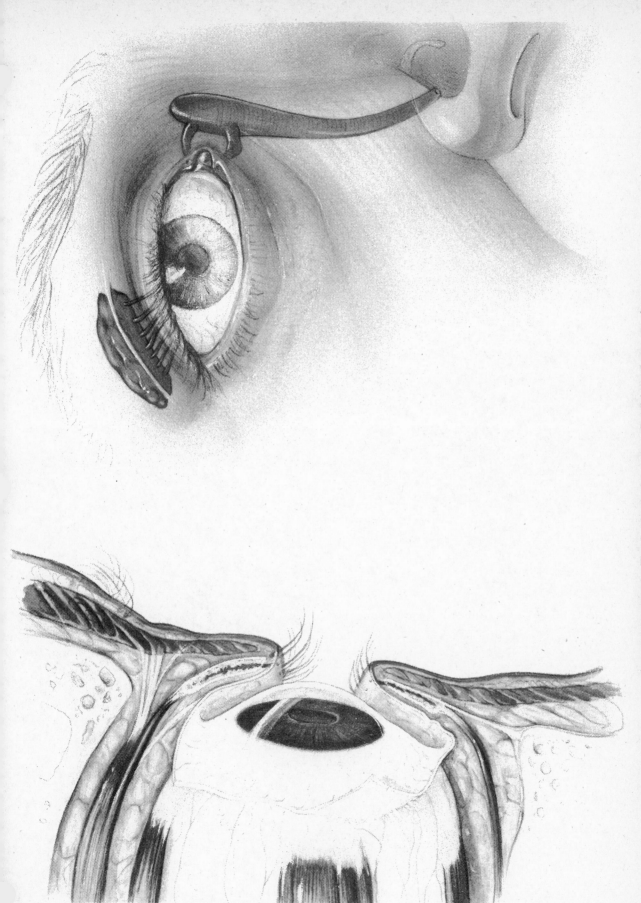

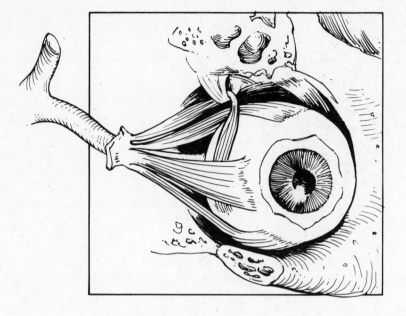

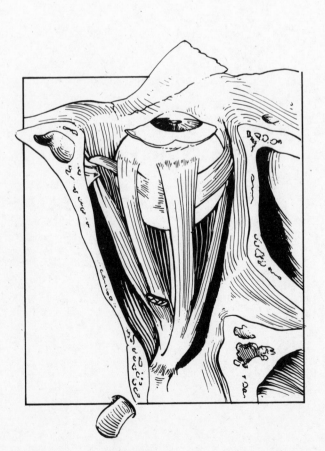

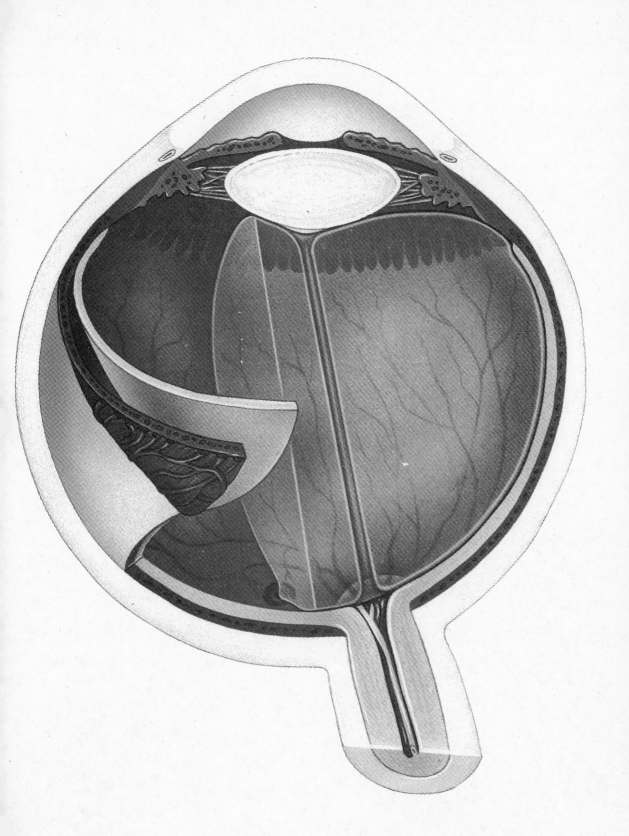

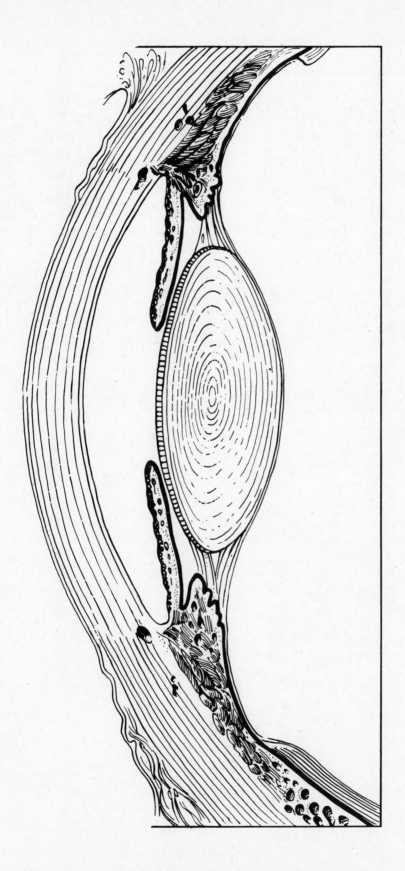

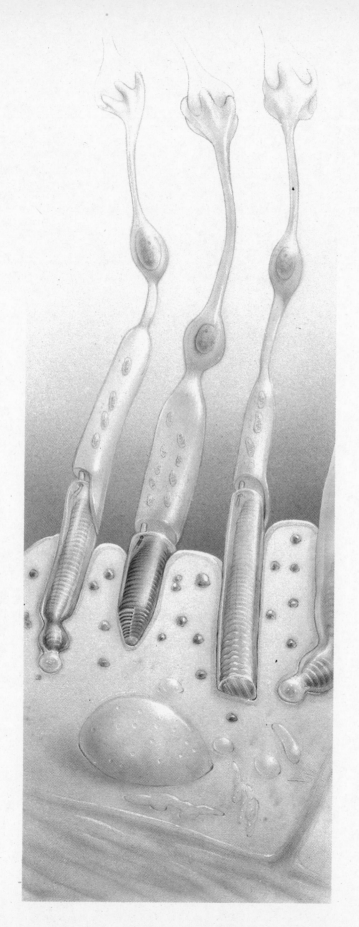

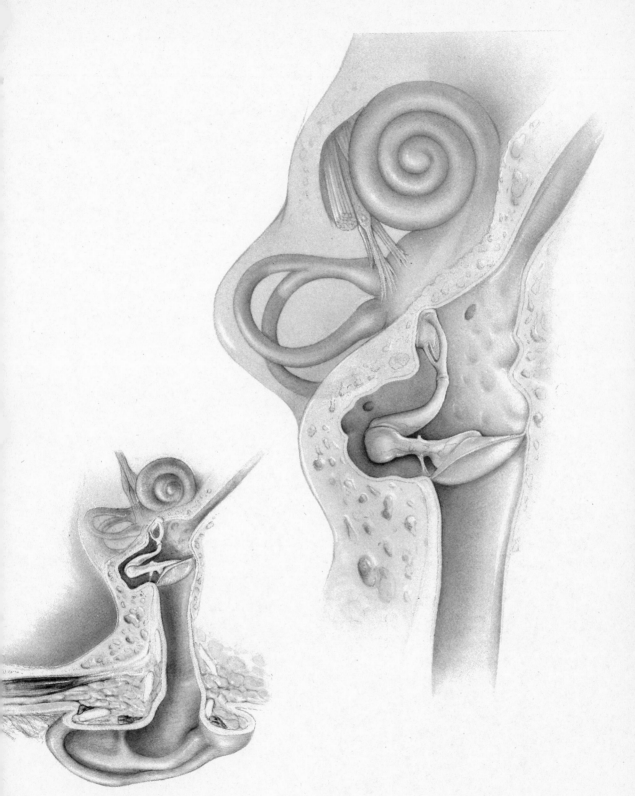

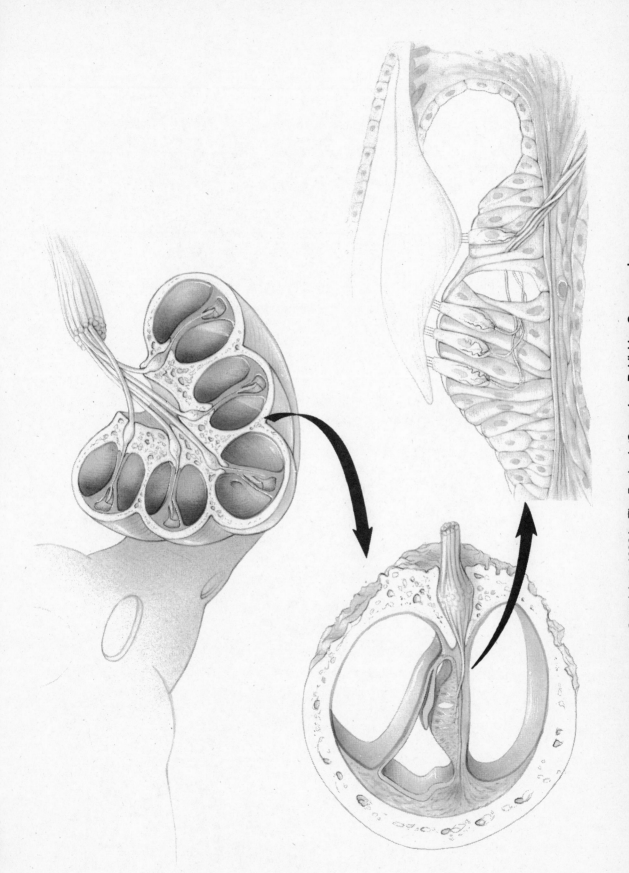

Test Bank

MATCHING QUESTIONS

Match the following:

a. Sclera
b. Retina
c. Lens
d. Choroid
e. Cornea
f. Iris

g. Aqueous humor
h. Ciliary muscle
i. Suspensory ligaments
j. Fovea centralis
k. Pupillary muscles
l. Extrinsic eye muscles

____ 1. The outer tough connective tissue covering of the eyeball.
____ 2. The muscle responsible for altering the shape of the lens.
____ 3. The vascular coat of the eyeball; deeply pigmented.
____ 4. The muscles that move the eyeball.
____ 5. The nervous layer of the eye.
____ 6. The structure most responsible for refracting light rays which enter the eye.
____ 7. Helps maintains the intraoccular pressure; located in the anterior part of the eye.
____ 8. Area of greatest visual acuity.

Qtype:»Memory   Outline:»II.C.   Text pp.»505-509
Answers:»1-a; 2-h; 3-d; 4-l; 5-b; 6-c; 7-g; 8-j

Match the following:

a. Glaucoma
b. Otitis media
c. Conduction deafness

d. Night blindness
e. Vertigo
f. Nerve deafness

____ 1. A condition that often results from a deficiency of Vitamin A.
____ 2. A condition of deafness which may result from otosclerosis.
____ 3. An inflammation of the lining of the middle ear.
____ 4. A loss of balance.
____ 5. A condition often leading to blindness due to increased intraoccular pressure.

Qtype:»Memory   Outline:»II.; III.   Text pp.»517-529
Answers:»1-d; 2-c; 3-b; 4-e; 5-a

Match the following:

a. Taste buds
b. Maculae

c. Crista ampularis
d. Superior nasal mucosa

____ 1. Gustatory cells are found in this structure.
____ 2. Hair cells receptive to changes in dynamic equilibrium are found in this structure.
____ 3. Hair cells receptive to changes in static equilibrium are found in this structure.
____ 4. The receptors of olfaction are found in this structure.

Qtype:»Memory   Outline:»I.A.,B.;III.   Text pp.»496-533
Answers:»1-a; 2-c; 3-b; 4-d

Match the following:

a. Crista
b. Cochlear duct
c. Auditory tube
d. Organ of Corti

e. Otoliths
f. Semicircular canals
g. Tympanic membrane
h. Vestibule

___ 1. Ear stones.
___ 2. Connects the middle ear with the nasopharynx.
___ 3. Separates external auditory canal from the middle ear.
___ 4. Contains utricle and saccule.
___ 5. Houses the spiral organ of Corti.
___ 6. The receptor organ for hearing.
___ 7. The central part of the bony labyrinth.
___ 8. A membrane that transmits sound vibrations to the ossicles.

Qtype:»Memory   Outline:»III.A.   Text pp.»521-525
Answers:»1-e; 2-c; 3-g; 4-h; 5-b; 6-d; 7-h; 8-g

Indicate whether the following conditions will cause:

(C) conduction deafness
(S) sensineural deafness
(T) tinnitus

___ 1. Can result from prolonged exposure to very loud rock music.
___ 2. Can result from the fusion of the ossicles.
___ 3. Can result from a lesion on the cochlear nerve.
___ 4. A possible side effect on medications such as aspirin.
___ 5. One of the most common causes of otitis media.
___ 6. Can result from impacted cerumen.

Qtype:»Concept   Outline:»III.C.   Text pp.»529-530
Answers:»1-S; 2-C; 3-S,T; 4-T; 5-C; 6-C

TRUE/FALSE QUESTIONS

1. A major feature of the vestibule is that it contains the saccule and utricle which in turn houses receptors for equilibrium.

        a. true   b. false

Qtype:»Concept   Outline:»III.A.3.b.   Text pp.»523
Answers:»true

2. The mucous membrane that lines the eyelids and is reflected over the anterior surface of the eyeball is the conjunctiva.

        a. true   b. false

Qtype:»Memory   Outline:»II.B.3.   Text pp.»503
Answers:»true

3. Vision is most acute when light rays are brought to focus on the optic disk.

        a. true   b. false

Qtype:»Concept   Outline:»II.C.1.   Text pp.»507
Answers:»false

---

4. Researchers have found that retinal ganglionic fields are of two types: on-center or off-center.

        a. true   b. false

Qtype:»Concept   Outline:»II.D.7.a.   Text pp.»519
Answers:»true

---

5. Without a functioning crista ampullaris, the semicircular canals would not have a function.

        a. true   b. false

Qtype:»Concept   Outline:»III.A.3.c.   Text pp.»524
Answers:»true

---

6. Except for the lateral rectus and superior oblique muscles, all extrinsic eye muscles are controlled by the trochlear nerve.

        a. true   b. false

Qtype:»Memory   Outline:»II.B.5.   Text pp.»504
Answers:»false

---

7. Unlike most other receptor cells found in the nasal passageways and in the ear, the photoreceptor cells are very resistant to damage such as heat or light.

        a. true   b. false

Qtype:»Concept   Outline:»II.D.3.a.   Text pp.»513
Answers:»false

---

8. Like the cornea, the lens is avascular.

        a. true   b. false

Qtype:»Concept   Outline:»II.C.3.a.   Text pp.»509
Answers:»true

---

9. The photoreceptor cells, rods and cones, generate action potentials rather than receptor end potentials.

        a. true   b. false

Qtype:»Concept   Outline:»II.D.4.   Text pp.»516
Answers:»false

---

10. Development of the ear begins in the three-week embryo.
                  a. true   b. false

Qtype:»Memory   Outline:»IV.A.   Text pp.»534
Answers:»true

---

11. Contraction of the ciliary muscle causes the lens to become more convex, thus bending the light less.
                  a. true   b. false

Qtype:»Concept   Outline:»II.D.2.   Text pp.»512
Answers:»false

---

12. Taste buds are found on filiform papilla.
                  a. true   b. false

Qtype:»Memory   Outline:»I.A.1.a.   Text pp.»497
Answers:»false

---

13. The optic disk is the spot where the optic nerve leaves the eyeball.
                  a. true   b. false

Qtype:»Concept   Outline:»II.C.1.c.   Text pp.»507
Answers:»true

---

14. Theoretically, an individual born without a middle ear would be able to hear by bone conduction with a hearing aid.
                  a. true   b. false

Qtype:»Concept   Outline:»III.C.1.   Text pp.»529
Answers:»true

---

15. Taste buds are located in projections of tissue called papillae.
                  a. true   b. false

Qtype:»Memory   Outline:»I.A.1.   Text pp.»497
Answers:»true

---

16. Aqueous humor drains from the anterior segment of the eye directly into the naso-lacrimal duct.
                  a. true   b. false

Qtype:»Memory   Outline:»II.C.2.   Text pp.»508-509
Answers:»false

---

17. When we move from darkness to bright light, retinal sensitivity is lost but visual acuity is gained.

　　　　　　　　　a. true　　　　　　　　　　　　b. false

Qtype:»Concept　　　Outline:»II.D.4.　　　　　　　　　Text pp.»517
Answers:»true

---

18. The lateral wall of the middle ear is formed primarily by the parietal bone.

　　　　　　　　　a. true　　　　　　　　　　　　b. false

Qtype:»Memory　　　Outline:»III.A.2.　　　　　　　　Text pp.»521
Answers:»false

---

19. The fluid contained within the membranous labyrinth is called endolymph.

　　　　　　　　　a. true　　　　　　　　　　　　b. false

Qtype:»Memory　　　Outline:»III.A.3.a.　　　　　　　Text pp.»523
Answers:»true

---

20. When one has a cold, swelling of the nasal mucosa may result in watery eyes or tearing due to lacrimal mucosal swelling.

　　　　　　　　　a. true　　　　　　　　　　　　b. false

Qtype:»Concept　　　Outline:»II.B.4.　　　　　　　　Text pp.»503
Answers:»true

---

21. The function of the lens of the eye is to diverge light rays and focus them on the retina.

　　　　　　　　　a. true　　　　　　　　　　　　b. false

Qtype:»Concept　　　Outline:»II.D.2.　　　　　　　　Text pp.»509
Answers:»false

---

22. High frequency sounds will stimulate the hair cells of the basilar membrane, near the oval window.

　　　　　　　　　a. true　　　　　　　　　　　　b. false

Qtype:»Concept　　　Outline:»III.B.3.　　　　　　　Text pp.»527
Answers:»true

---

23. The structure which allows equalization of the pressure in the middle ear with that outside the body, is the external auditory meatus.

　　　　　　　　　a. true　　　　　　　　　　　　b. false

Qtype:»Memory　　　Outline:»III.A.2.e.　　　　　　　Text pp.»522
Answers:»false

---

24. The bending of light rays is called refraction.
          a. true   b. false

Qtype:»Memory   Outline:»II.D.1.b.   Text pp.»510
Answers:»true

---

25. The anterior chamber of the eye is filled with vitreous humor.
          a. true   b. false

Qtype:»Memory   Outline:»II.C.2.b.   Text pp.»508
Answers:»false

---

26. Fibers of the olfactory nerve project through the cribiform plate of the ethmoid bone.
          a. true   b. false

Qtype:»Memory   Outline:»I.B.1.   Text pp.»499
Answers:»true

---

27. Dry air is important in the reception of the sense of smell.
          a. true   b. false

Qtype:»Concept   Outline:»I.B.3.   Text pp.»500
Answers:»false

---

28. The cortical center for olfactory sensation is located in the limbic system of the brain.
          a. true   b. false

Qtype:»Memory   Outline:»I.B.4.c.   Text pp.»
Answers:»false

---

29. The structure of the eyeball, which prevents excessive scattering of light within the eye, is the choroid layer.
          a. true   b. false

Qtype:»Memory   Outline:»II.C.1.b.   Text pp.»506
Answers:»true

---

30. The structure which acts to control the amount of light entering the eye is the iris.
          a. true   b. false

Qtype:»Memory   Outline:»II.C.1.b.   Text pp.»506
Answers:»true

---

31. In order for sound to reach the organ of Corti, the stapes must vibrate the round window, and set the endolymph in motion.

                  a. true   b. false

Qtype:»Concept   Outline:»III.B.3.   Text pp.»527
Answers:»false

---

32. Sound is generally perceived in the cerebral cortex of the occipital lobe.

                  a. true   b. false

Qtype:»Concept   Outline:»III.B.5.   Text pp.»528
Answers:»false

---

33. Presbycusis is a disorder commonly seen in the elderly but now seen in younger people who listen to excessively loud rock music for long periods of time.

                  a. true   b. false

Qtype:»Concept   Outline:»IV.C.   Text pp.»536
Answers:»true

MULTIPLE-CHOICE QUESTIONS

1. What is the main function of the rods in the eye?
   a. depth perception
   b. color vision
   c. vision in dim light
   d. accommodation for near vision
   e. refraction

Qtype:»Concept   Outline:»II.C.1.   Text pp.»507
Answers:»c

---

2. What structure regulates the amount of light passing to the visual receptors of the eye?
   a. aqueous humor   d. iris
   b. vitreous humor   e. lens
   c. cornea

Qtype:»Memory   Outline:»II.C.1.b.   Text pp.»506
Answers:»d

---

3. Which pairing of terms is incorrectly related?
   a. frequency - loudness
   b. quality - multiple frequencies
   c. frequency - pitch
   d. frequency - wavelength
   e. All of the above are incorrectly paired.

   Qtype:»Concept   Outline:»III.B.1.   Text pp.»526
   Answers:»a

---

4. Olfactory cells and taste buds are normally stimulated by:
   a. the movement of otoliths.
   b. stretching of the receptor cells.
   c. substances in solution.
   d. movement of a cupula.
   e. mechanical stimulation only.

   Qtype:»Memory   Outline:»I.A.3.   Text pp.»498
   Answers:»c

---

5. Which of the following could **not** be seen as one looks into the eye with an
   ophthalmoscope?
   a. macula lutea   d. optic disk
   b. optic chiasma   e. iris
   c. fovea centralis

   Qtype:»Concept   Outline:»II.C.1.c.   Text pp.»506-507
   Answers:»b

---

6. Receptors for hearing are located in the:
   a. cochlea.   d. tympanic membrane.
   b. middle ear.   e. vestibule.
   c. semicircular canals.

   Qtype:»Memory   Outline:»III.A.3.d.   Text pp.»524
   Answers:»a

---

7. Cortical processing involves ____ population(s) of cortical neurons:
   a. 1.   d. 4.
   b. 2.   e. 5.
   c. 3.

   Qtype:»Memory   Outline:»II.D.7.   Text pp.»521
   Answers:»b

---

8. Presbyopia is due to:
   a. loss of elasticity of the lens.
   b. unequal curvature of refracting surfaces.
   c. an eyeball that is too long.
   d. a flattened cornea.
   e. None of the above are correct.

   Qtype:»Concept   Outline:»II.D.2.c.   Text pp.»512
   Answers:»a

9. The oil component found in tears is produced by the:
   a. lacrimal glands.   d. endocrine gland.
   b. meibomian glands.   e. ciliary gland.
   c. conjunctiva.

   Qtype:»Memory   Outline:»II.B.2.e.   Text pp.»502
   Answers:»b

10. The receptor for static equilibrium is the:
    a. semicircular canals.   d. cochlear duct.
    b. macula.   e. middle ear.
    c. utricle.

    Qtype:»Memory   Outline:»III.D.2.a.   Text pp.»530
    Answers:»b

11. Which of the following is **not** important in maintaining the balance of the body?
    a. the semicircular canals
    b. the muscle stretch receptors
    c. visual impulses
    d. the otoliths
    e. All of the above are important.

    Qtype:»Concept   Outline:»III.D.1.   Text pp.»530
    Answers:»e

12. Part of "taste" derives from stimulation of all the following except:
    a. gustatory cells.
    b. olfactory receptors.
    c. pain receptors.
    d. temperature receptors.
    e. All of the above affect taste.

    Qtype:»Concept   Outline:»I.A.2.   Text pp.»499
    Answers:»e

13. The cells of the retina in which action potentials are generated are the:
   a. rods.
   b. bipolar cells.
   c. ganglion cells.
   d. amacrine cells.
   e. cones only.

   Qtype:»Memory   Outline:»II.C.1.c.   Text pp.»506
   Answers:»c

---

14. Depth perception involves which of the following?
   a. coordination of activity of both eyes
   b. use of visual cues
   c. projection of inputs from both eyes to the cortical cells
   d. cortical fusion of images from both eyes
   e. All of the above are correct.

   Qtype:»Concept   Outline:»II.D.6.   Text pp.»518
   Answers:»e

---

15. During dark adaptation:
   a. rhodopsin accumulates in the rods.
   b. the rate of rhodopsin breakdown is accelerated.
   c. the sensitivity of the retina decreases.
   d. the cones are activated.
   e. Two of the above are correct.

   Qtype:»Concept   Outline:»II.D.4.c.   Text pp.»517
   Answers:»a

---

16. During embryonic development, the retina of the eye develops from:
   a. the surface ectoderm.
   b. an outpocketing of the diencephalon of the brain.
   c. the mesoderm.
   d. the mesoderm and the ectoderm.
   e. None of the above are correct.

   Qtype:»Memory   Outline:»IV.A.   Text pp.»534
   Answers:»b

---

17. Tinnitis, vertigo, and gradual hearing loss typify the disorder called:
   a. conjunctivitis.
   b. Meniere's syndrome.
   c. strabissimus.
   d. motion sickness.

   Qtype:»Concept   Outline:»III.C.3.   Text pp.»529
   Answers:»b

---

18. The olfactory receptor cells can be characterized by all <u>except</u>:
   a. they are ciliated.
   b. they are unipolar neurons.
   c. they are chemoreceptors.
   d. they have a short life span of about 60 days.
   e. All of the above characterize olfactory receptors.

   Qtype:»Concept   Outline:»I.B.   Text pp.»499-501
   Answers:»b

---

19. The eyelids house which of the following?
   a. tarsal glands
   b. tarsal plates
   c. orbicularis oculi muscles
   d. glands of Zeis
   e. All of the above are correct.

   Qtype:»Memory   Outline:»II.B.2.   Text pp.»502
   Answers:»e

---

20. The region of the tongue with the greatest sensitivity to sweet taste is the:
   a. anterior aspect.
   b. lateral edges.
   c. posterior aspect.
   d. inferior aspect.
   e. All areas are equally sensitive.

   Qtype:»Memory   Outline:»I.A.1.   Text pp.»498
   Answers:»a

---

21. Farsightedness is more properly called:
   a. myopia.   d. emmetropia.
   b. presbyopia.   e. hypopia
   c. hyperopia.

   Qtype:»Memory   Outline:»II.D.2.   Text pp.»512
   Answers:»c

---

22. Visual processing in the thalamus involves:
   a. depth perception.
   b. high-acuity vision.
   c. night vision.
   d. Two of the above are correct.
   e. None of the above are correct.

   Qtype:»Concept   Outline:»II.D.7.b.   Text pp.»520
   Answers:»d

---

23. Lacrimal solutions normally contain which of the following?
    a. lysozyme
    b. antibodies
    c. enkephalins
    d. mucus
    e. All of the above are correct.

      Qtype:»Memory   Outline:»II.B.4.e.   Text pp.»503
      Answers:»e

24. Inhibitory cells in the olfactory bulbs are called:
    a. mitral cells.   d. basal cells.
    b. granule cells.   e. fibroblasts.
    c. sustentacular cells.

      Qtype:»Memory   Outline:»I.B.4.a.   Text pp.»500
      Answers:»b

25. Which of the following structures is **not** part of the external ear?
    a. pinna
    b. external auditory meatus
    c. tympanic membrane
    d. oval window
    e. All of the above are part of the external ear.

      Qtype:»Memory   Outline:»III.A.1.   Text pp.»521
      Answers:»d

26. Nerve fibers from the medial aspect of each eye:
    a. cross over to the opposite side at the chiasma.
    b. pass posteriorly without crossing over at the chiasma.
    c. divide at the chiasma, some crossing and some not crossing.
    d. never reach the cortex.
    e. None of the above are correct.

      Qtype:»Memory   Outline:»II.D.5.a.   Text pp.»518
      Answers:»a

27. Ordinarily, it is not possible to transplant tissues from one person to another, yet corneas can be transplanted without tissue rejection. This is because the cornea:
    a. is not a living tissue.
    b. has no nerve supply.
    c. has no blood supply except around the periphery.
    d. is exposed and easily accessible.
    e. does not contain connective tissue.

      Qtype:»Concept   Outline:»II.C.1.a.   Text pp.»505
      Answers:»c

28. The oval window is connected directly to which passageway?
    a. eustachian tube
    b. external auditory meatus
    c. scala vestibuli
    d. scala tympani
    e. auditory tube

    Qtype:»Memory   Outline:»III.A.3.d.   Text pp.»524
    Answers:»c

_____

29. There are three layers of neurons in the retina. The axons of which of these neuron layers forms the optic nerves?
    a. bipolar cells
    b. ganglion cells
    c. cone cells
    d. rod cells

    Qtype:»Memory   Outline:»II.C.1.c.   Text pp.»506
    Answers:»b

_____

30. The first "way station" in the visual pathway from the eye, after there has been partial cross-over of the fibers in the optic chiasma, is:
    a. the superior colliculi.
    b. the lateral geniculate nuclei of the thalamus.
    c. the visual cortex.
    d. the temporal lobe.
    e. None of the above are correct.

    Qtype:»Concept   Outline:»II.D.6.   Text pp.»518
    Answers:»b

_____

31. An accident patient found that he could not easily detect sweet, sour, or salty substances. Which cranial nerve was probably damaged?
    a. facial
    b. glossopharyngeal
    c. vagus
    d. oculomotor
    e. cranial nerve X

    Qtype:»Application Outline:»I.A.4.a.   Text pp.»498
    Answers:»a

_____

32. The opsins found in cone cells are called:
    a. rhodopsins.
    b. photopsins.
    c. scotopsins.
    d. metarhodopsins.
    e. conopsins

    Qtype:»Memory   Outline:»II.D.4.b.   Text pp.»516
    Answers:»b

_____

33. Which of the following is specifically associated with the cochlea?
    a. saccule
    b. crista ampullaris
    c. organ of Corti
    d. stapedius
    e. two of these are associated

    Qtype:»Memory   Outline:»III.A.3.d.   Text pp.»524
    Answers:»c

34. Which of the following do **not** appear to be especially significant in the equilibrium pathways to the brain?
    a. cerebellum
    b. vestibular nuclear complex
    c. flocculonodular node
    d. Wernicke's area
    e. All of the above are significant.

    Qtype:»Concept   Outline:»III.D.4.   Text pp.»533
    Answers:»d

35. An essential part of the maculae involved in static equilibrium is(are) the:
    a. organ of Corti.
    b. cupula.
    c. scala media.
    d. otoliths
    e. Two of the above are correct.

    Qtype:»Memory   Outline:»III.D.2.b.   Text pp.»530
    Answers:»d

36. Which of the following is (are) true about gustatory receptors?
    a. In order for a chemical to be sensed, it must be hydrophobic.
    b. The receptors generate an action potential in response to chemical stimuli.
    c. Complete adaptation occurs in about one to five minutes.
    d. All gustatory receptors have the same threshold for activation.
    e. All of the above are correct.

    Qtype:»Concept   Outline:»I.A.3.   Text pp.»498
    Answers:»c

37. Select the correct statement(s) about gustation.
    1. Activation of gustatory receptors initiates a reflex causing an increase in gastric secretion.
    2. All substances are equal in the ability to generate a sense of smell.
    3. Some chemical stimuli can initiate reflex vomiting.
    a. 1 only
    b. 2 only
    c. 3 only
    d. 1 and 3
    e. 2 and 3

    Qtype:»Concept   Outline:»I.A.4.   Text pp.»499
    Answers:»d

38. Select the correct statement about olfaction.
    a. Olfactory receptors have a high degree of specificity toward a single type of chemical.
    b. Some of the sensation of olfaction is actually one of pain.
    c. Substances must be volatile and hydrophobic in order to activate olfactory receptors.
    d. Olfactory adaptation is only due to fading of receptor cell response.
    e. None of the above are correct.

    Qtype:»Memory   Outline:»I.B.2.,3.   Text pp.»499-500
    Answers:»b

39. Photoreceptors:
    a. replicate to replace damaged cells, in order to maintain normal vision.
    b. package visual pigment in membrane bound discs, which increase the efficiency of light trapping.
    c. called rods, contain discs that become progressively smaller toward the end of the cell.
    d. possess an inner segment which is the receptor region.
    e. called cones, possess a short conical inner segment.

    Qtype:»Memory   Outline:»II.D.3.a.   Text pp.»513
    Answers:»b

40. Select the most correct statement(s) about vision.
    1. The fovea centralis contains a large number of photoreceptors per unit area.
    2. The macula lutea contains mainly rods which allows a high degree of light sensitivity.
    3. A large fraction of the visual field is in sharp focus at any given instant.
    a. 1 only
    b. 2 only
    c. 3 only
    d. 1 and 3
    e. 2 and 3

    Qtype:»Concept   Outline:»II.C.1.c.   Text pp.»507
    Answers:»a

41. Which of the following is(are) true about light and vision?
    a. Human photoreceptors respond to light in the 100-300 nm range.
    b. When we "see" the color of an object, all light is being absorbed by that object except the color being experienced.
    c. Light is a form of electromagnetic radiation that slows down as it enters a medium of relative less density.
    d. The greater the incident angle of light striking a refractive surface, the lesser the amount of light bending.
    e. An optical lens is able to reflect but not refract light.

    Qtype:»Concept   Outline:»II.D.1.a.   Text pp.»510
    Answers:»b

42. The closest point at which one can clearly focus is:
    1. called the near point of vision.
    2. affected by the refractive ability of the lens.
    3. enhanced by constriction of the pupil.
    a. 1 only   d. 1 and 3
    b. 2 only   e. 1, 2, and 3
    c. 3 only

    Qtype:»Memory   Outline:»II.D.2.c.   Text pp.»511-512
    Answers:»e

43. When rhodopsin absorbs light, several changes result. Place the following substances in correct sequence.
    1. lumirhodopsin
    2. prelumirhodopsin
    3. metarhodopsin
    4. pararhodopsin.
    a. 4,3,2,1   d. 4,1,2,3
    b. 1,2,3,4   e. 2,1,3,4
    c. 2,1,4,3

    Qtype:»Memory   Outline:»II.D.3.b.   Text pp.»515-516
    Answers:»e

44. Which of the following is(are) true about photoreceptors?
    a. Rods absorb light throughout the visual spectrum but confer only gray tone vision.
    b. In dim light, images are focused directly on the rods in the fovea centralis.
    c. Cones are nondiscriminatory photoreceptors.
    d. Three types of color sensitive photoreceptors exist: red, green, and yellow.
    e. If all cones are stimulated equally, all colors are absorbed by the cones and the color perceived is black.

    Qtype:»Concept   Outline:»II.D.4.   Text pp.»515-517
    Answers:»a

45. Mechanisms of retinal processing include:
    a. hyperpolarization of photoreceptors by light.
    b. a depolarizing bipolar neuron in the center of a receptive field, exciting a ganglion cell.
    c. the activity of bipolar neurons in the field periphery subject to lateral inhibition.
    d. amacrine cells exerting inhibitory effects on ganglion cells.
    e. All of the above are correct.

    Qtype:»Memory   Outline:»II.D.7.   Text pp.»519-520
    Answers:»e

46. Select the correct statement about equilibrium.
    a. The weight of the endolymph, contained within the semicircular canals against the maculae, is responsible for static equilibrium.
    b. Cristae respond to angular acceleration.
    c. Hair cells of both types of equilibrium hyperpolarize only, resulting in an increased rate of impulse transmission.
    d. Due to dynamic equilibrium, movement can be perceived if rotation of the body continues at a constant rate.
    e. Cristae are static equilibrium receptors.

    Qtype:»Concept   Outline:»III.D.   Text pp.»530-533
    Answers:»b

47. During vestibular nystagmus:
    1. eyes drift relatively slowly in the opposite direction of rotation.
    2. eyes jump rapidly in the direction of rotation.
    3. eye movements continue until endolymph movement ceases.
    a. 1 only   d. 1 and 3
    b. 2 only   e. 1, 2, and 3
    c. 3 only

    Qtype:»Memory   Outline:»III.D.3.d.   Text pp.»532
    Answers:»e

48. Choose the most correct statement about sound.
    a. Sounds can be transmitted through a vacuum.
    b. A sound wave and light beam emitted at the same time and place would both strike an object some distance away at the same time.
    c. High frequency correlates with low pitch.
    d. Increased amplitude corresponds to increased loudness.
    e. A one decibel increase represents a tenfold increase in sound intensity.

    Qtype:»Concept   Outline:»III.B.1.   Text pp.»525-526
    Answers:»d

49. Transmission of sound to the inner ear:
1. involves propagation of sound waves through a vacuum.
2. depends on vibration of the tympanic membrane, at a lower frequency than the initial sound wave.
3. involves amplification of the sound striking the tympanic membrane.

a. 1 only
b. 2 only
c. 3 only

d. 1 and 3
e. 2 and 3

Qtype:»Memory   Outline:»III.B.2.   Text pp.»526
Answers:»c

50. Transduction of a sound wave into electrical impulses involves:
a. low frequency sounds traveling a short distance into the cochlea.
b. transmission of force through a compressible fluid.
c. resonance of the tectorial membrane, in response to specific frequencies in specific areas.
d. hairs of the hair cells embedded in the basilar membrane.
e. the generation of receptor potentials.

Qtype:»Concept   Outline:»III.B.3.   Text pp.»527-528
Answers:»e

51. Auditory processing includes:
1. perception of pitch.
2. perception of loudness.
3. localization of sound.

a. 1 only
b. 2 only
c. 3 only

d. 1 and 3
e. 1, 2, and 3

Qtype:»Memory   Outline:»III.B.6.   Text pp.»529
Answers:»e

52. Select the correct statement about basic eye movements.
1. Saccades are small jerky movements that move the eye rapidly from one point to another.
2. Scanning movements allow us to follow objects while we move our heads.
3. Tracking movements specifically refers the eyes following stationary objects while we are moving.

a. 1 only
b. 2 only
c. 3 only

d. 1 and 3
e. 1, 2, and 3

Qtype:»Memory   Outline:»II.B.5.   Text pp.»504
Answers:»e

53. If the left eye were lost in an accident, which of the following would be correct?
    1. Peripheral vision on the left side would be lost.
    2. Depth perception would be reduced by one half.
    3. The right eye would eventually compensate for the initial loss in depth perception
    a. 1 only   d. 1 and 3
    b. 2 only   e. 2 and 3
    c. 3 only

Qtype:»Concept   Outline:»II.D.6.c.   Text pp.»518
Answers:»a

SHORT-ANSWER QUESTIONS

1. Trace the pathway of sound as it enters the external ear until it is perceived in the brain.

Qtype:»Concept   Outline:»III.B.   Text pp.»525-529
Answers:»A sound wave passing through the external auditory canal, causes the eardrum
to vibrate at the same frequency as the wave. The ossicles amplify and deliver vibrations
to the oval window. Pressure waves in the cochlear fluids causes basilar membrane
resonance which stimulates the hair cells of the organ of Corti. Impulses are then
generated along the cochlear nerve which travels to the cochlear nuclei of the medulla,
and from there, through several brain stem nuclei to the auditory cortex of the brain.

2. Contrast light and dark adaptation and include the role of the rods and cones.

Qtype:»Concept   Outline:»II.D.4.c.   Text pp.»517
Answers:»Rods respond to low intensity light which provides night and peripheral vision
while cones are bright light, high discrimination receptors that provide color vision. During
light adaptation, rods are inactivated and as cones respond to the high intensity light, high
visual acuity results. In dark adaptation, cones do not function (visual acuity decreases)
and rod function resumes when sufficient rhodopsin accumulates.

3. What is the chemical composition of the rod pigment, rhodopsin, and how does it appear
   to act in the reception of light.

Qtype:»Concept   Outline:»II.D.4.a.   Text pp.»515
Answers:»Rhodopsin is a combination of retinal and scotopsin. Retinal is chemically
related to vitamin A and is synthesized from it. Retinal can form a variety of three
dimensional forms called isomers. Scotopsin is a complex opsin protein, which combines
with the 11-cis retinal to form rhodopsin. The light triggered changes in retinal causes
hyperpolarization of the rods. This happens because the light turns off sodium entry,
which then inhibits the release of neurotransmitter, thus turning off electrical signals.

4. Explain the role of the endolymph of the semicircular canals in activating the receptors during angular motion.

>   Qtype:»Concept   Outline:»III.D.3.c.   Text pp.»531-532
>   Answers:»The crista ampularis responds to changes in the velocity of head movement
>   (angular acceleration). The crista consists of a tuft of hair cells whose microvilli are
>   embedded in the gelatinous cupula. Rotational movements causes the endolymph to flow
>   in the opposite direction thus bending the cupula and exciting the hair cells.

CLINICAL QUESTIONS

1. A 60-year old woman is experiencing vertigo. She ignores the symptoms initially but now her attacks are accompanied by severe nausea and vomiting, and following an attack, she hears a crackling in her ears that causes temporary deafness for some time after. What do you think her problem is and what is its suspected cause?

>   Qtype:»Application Outline:»III.C.3.   Text pp.»529-530
>   Answers:»She most likely has a condition know as Meniere's syndrome. It affects both
>   the semicircular canals and the cochlea. The cause of the syndrome is uncertain, but it
>   may result from distortion of the membranous labyrinth by excessive endolymph
>   accumulation. Less severe cases can usually be managed by antimotion drugs. For more
>   debilitating attacks, salt restriction and diuretics are used to decrease overall extracellular
>   fluid volumes.

2. Roger went for his yearly eye examination and was informed that his intraocular pressure was slightly elevated (at 22mm Hg). The physician expressed concern over this condition and noted that if the condition got worse, eyedrops would be merited. Why is the doctor concerned over the elevated intraocular pressure...that is, what is wrong with Roger's eyes, and what are the possible consequences of this condition? Explain the function of eyedrops used for therapy.

>   Qtype:»Application Outline:»II.C.2.b.   Text pp.»509
>   Answers:»If the drainage of the aqueous humor is blocked, pressure within the eye can
>   increase causing compression of the retina and optic nerve, resulting in a condition called
>   glaucoma. The resulting destruction of the neural structures causes blindness unless the
>   condition is detected early. Early glaucoma can be treated with eyedrops that increase
>   the rate of aqueous humor drainage.

3. Mary, a 75-year old grandmother, complained that her vision was becoming obscured. Upon examination by an ophthalmologist she was told she had cataracts. What are they, how do they occur, and how are they treated?

>   Qtype:»Application Outline:»II.C.3.d.   Text pp.»509
>   Answers:»A cataract is a clouding of the lens which causes the world to appear distorted,
>   as if looking through frosted glass. Some cataracts are congenital, but most are related to
>   age related hardening and thickening of the lens, or a possible consequence of diabetes
>   mellitus. The direct cause is probably inadequate delivery of nutrients to the deeper lens
>   fibers. The metabolic changes that result are thought to promote unfolding of the lens
>   proteins. The lens can be removed and replaced with an artificial lens.

4. After head trauma during an automobile accident, a man has anosmia. Define anosmia. Why is this condition fairly common after such injuries and in cases of severe nasal cavity inflammation?

Qtype:»Application Outline:»I.C.1.   Text pp.»501
Answers:»Anosmia means the loss of chemical sense of smell due to some olfactory disorder. Most result from head injuries or nasal cavity inflammations, allergies, smoking, and aging. The olfactory pathways are very sensitive to irritations or to damage, especially if the ethmoid bones have been damaged due to trauma. In many cases the problem is a lack of zinc, which appears to be a necessary growth factor for the regeneration of new olfactory receptors.

Guide to Audiovisual Resources

ACR	American College of Radiology, 20 N. Wacker Drive, Chicago, IL 60606
ACS	American Cancer Society, 19 West 56th Street, New York, NY 10019 (212) 586-8700
AEF	American Educational Films, 3807 Dickerson Road, Nashville, TN 37207 (615) 868-2040
AF	Academy Films, P.O. Box 1023, Venice, CA 90291
AFI	Association Films, 799 Stevenson Street, San Francisco, CA 94103
AIF	Australian Instructional Films, 39 Pitt Street, Sydney, Australia
AMA	American Medical Association, 535 N. Dearborn, Chicago, IL 60610 (800) 621-8335
APH	Alfred Higgins Productions, 9100 Sunset Blvd., Los Angeles, CA 90069
ASFT	Association-Sterling, 8615 Directors Row, Dallas, TX 75240
BARR	Barr Films, 12801 Schabarum Ave., Irwindale, CA 91706 (818) 338-7878
BFA	BFA Films and Videos, 468 Park Ave. South, New York, NY 10016 (800) 221-1274
BM	Biology Media, P.O. Box 10205, Berkeley, CA 94710
BNF	Benchmark Films, Inc., 145 Scarborough Road, Briarcliff Manor, NY 10510 (914) 762-3838
BYU	Brigham Young University, Audio-Visual Services, 101 Fletcher Building, Provo, UT 84602 (801) 378-4071
CA	Career Aids, 20417 Nordhuff St., Post AH98, Chatsworth, CA 91311 (213) 341-8200
CBS	Carolina Biological Supply Company, 2700 York Road, Burlington, NC 27215 (800) 334-5551
CCM	CCM Films, Inc. Distributed by: Films, Inc., 5547 Ravenswood Ave., Chicago, IL 60640
CCMI	Classroom Consortia Media, Inc.
CDL	Cambridge Development Laboratory, Inc., 42 4th Ave., Waltham, MA 02154
CDR	Center for Devices and Radiological Health, Training Resources Center, 5300 Fishers Lane, Rockville, MD 20857 (301) 443-4647
CF	Churchill Media, 12210 Nebraska Ave., Los Angeles, CA 90025 (800) 334-7830
CFI	Counselor Films, Inc., 1728 Cherry St., Philadelphia, PA 19103
CHM	Cleveland Health Museum, 8911 Euclid Ave., Cleveland, OH 44106
CIBA	Ciba Pharmaceutical Company, Medical Communications Dept., 556 Morris Ave., Summit, NJ 07901
CIF	Coronet/MTI Film and Video, Supplementary Education Group, Simon and Schuster Communications, 108 Wilmot Rd., Deerfield, IL 60015-9990 (800) 621-2131
COND	Conduit, P.O. Box 388, Iowa City, IA 52244
CRM	CRM Films, 2215 Faraday, Carlsbad, CA 92008 (800) 421-0833
DA	Document Associates/The Cinema Guild, 1697 Broadway, Suite 802, New York, NY 10019 (212) 246-5522
EBE	Encyclopedia Britannica Educational Corporation, 310 South Michigan Ave., Chicago, IL 60604 (800) 621-3900
EI	Educational Images (see EIL below)
EIL	Educational Images Limited, P.O. Box 3456, Elmira, NY 14905 (607) 732-1090
EL	Eli Lilly and Company, Medical Division, Indianapolis, IN 46206 (317) 261-2000
FAD	F. A. Davis Company, 1915 Arch St., Philadelphia, PA 19103 (215) 568-2270

FHS	Films for the Humanities and Sciences, Inc., P.O. Box 2053, Princeton, NJ 08540 (800) 257-5126
HP	Hoechst-Roussel Pharmaceuticals, Rt. #202-206N, Somerville, NJ 08876 (201) 685-2648
HR	Harper and Row Publishers. Distributed by: MTI Teleprograms, 108 Wilmot Rd, Deerfield, IL 60015 (212) 207-7000
HRM	Human Relations Media, 175 Tompkins Ave., Pleasantville, NY 10570 (800) 431-2050
IBIS	IBIS Media (now HRM above)
ICI	Imperial Chemicals Industries, Inc., P.O. Box 1274, 151 South St., Stamford, CT 06904
ICIA	ICI America, Inc., Concord Pike & Murphy Rd., Wilmington, DE 19899 (302) 575-3275
IFB	International Film Bureau, 332 S. Michigan Ave., Chicago, IL 60604 (312) 427-4545
IOWA	Iowa State University Media Resources Center, 121 Pearson Hall, Ames, IA 50011 (515) 294-1540
IP	Iwanami Productions, Inc., 22-2 Kanda Misakicho, Chiyoda-Ku, Tokyo, Japan
IU	Indiana University Audio-Visual Center, Bloomington, IN 47405-5901 (800) 552-8620
JBL	J.B. Lippincott, East Washington Square, Philadelphia, PA 19105 (800) 523-2945
JJ	Johnson and Johnson, Grandview Road, Skillman, NJ 08558
JW	John Wiley and Sons, Inc., 605 Third Ave., New York, NY 10158 (212) 850-6276
LPI	Lawren Productions, Inc., 930 Pitner Ave., Evanston, IL 60202 (800) 323-9084
MAP	Medical Arts Production
MC	Mayo Clinic, Section of Photography, 200 S.W. First St., Rochester, MN 55905 (507) 284-2511
McG	McGraw-Hill Book Co., Inc., Text-Film Division, 1221 Avenue of the Americas, New York, NY 10020 (see CRM above)
MF	Milner-Fenwick, Inc., 2125 Greenspring Drive, Timonium, MD 21093 (800) 638-8652
MG	Media Guild, 11722 Sorrento Valley Rd., Suite E, San Diego, CA 92121 (619) 755-9191
MGHT	McGraw-Hill Films (see CRM above)
MI	Medcom, Inc., 1633 Broadway, New York, NY 10019
NEIF	National Educational and Information Films, Ltd., National House, Tullock Rd., Apollo Bunder, Bombay 1, India
NET	Nebraska Educational Television Council for Higher Education, Inc., P.O. Box 83111, Lincoln, NE 68501 (402) 472-3611
NGS	National Geographic Society, 1145 17th St. N.W., Washington, DC 20036 (800) 368-2728
NTA	National Teaching Aids, 120 Fulton Ave., Garden City Park, NY 11040
NYAM	New York Academy of Medicine, 2 East 103rd St., New York, NY 10029
PAR	Paramount Communications. Distributed by: AIMS Media, 9710 DeSoto Ave., Chatsworth, CA 91311 (818) 773-4300
PE	Perennial Education, Inc., 930 Pitner Avenue, Evanston, IL 60202 (800) 323-9084
PFP	Pyramid Films and Videos, P.O. Box 1048, Santa Monica, CA 90406 (800) 421-2304
PHM	Prentice-Hall Media. Distributed by: Vocational Media Associates, P.O. Box 1000, Mount Kisco, New York, NY 10549 (800) 431-1242
PLP	Projected Learning Programs, Inc., P.O. Box 3008, Paradise, CA 95969 (916) 893-4223

PMR	Peter M. Robeck and Co., Inc. Distributed by: Time-Life Films, Inc. (see TL below)
POLY	Polymorph Films, Inc., 118 South Street, Boston, MA 02111 (617) 542-2004
PSP	Popular Science Publishing Company, 355 Lexington Ave., New York, NY 10017
PYR	Pyramid Films and Videos, P.O. Box 1048, Santa Monica, CA 90406 (800) 421-2304
QUE	Queue, Inc., 562 Boston Ave., Bridgeport, CT 06610
REX	REX Educational Resources Company, P.O. Box 2379, Burlington, NC 27216
RJB	Robert J. Brady Company, 130 Q Street N.E., Washington, DC 20002
RL	Roche Biomedical Lab, Inc., 1447 York Ct., Burlington, NC 27215 (919) 584-5171
SC	Scherring Corporation, 1011 Morris Avenue, Union, NJ 07083 (201) 558-4000
SEF	Sterling Educational Films, 241 E. 34th St., New York, NY 10016 (212) 779-0202
SM	Science and Mankind, Inc., P.O. Box 1000, Mount Kisco, NY 10549 (800) 431-1242
SQ	E.R. Squibb and Sons, Inc., P.O. Box 4500, Princeton, NJ 08543-4500
SU	Syracuse University Film Library, 1455 E. Colvin St., Collendale Campus, Syracuse, NY 13210
TC	Trainex Corp., 12601 Industry St., Garden Grove, CA 92641 (714) 898-2561
TF	Teaching Films, Inc., 930 Pitner Ave., Evanston, IL 60202 (312) 328-6700
TL	Time-Life Films (see Time-Life Video below)
TLV	Time-Life Video. Distributed by: Ambrose Video Publishing, Inc., 381 Park Avenue South, Suite 1601, New York, NY 10016 (212) 696-4545
TNF	The National Foundation - March of Dimes, Professional Film Library, c/o Association Inc., 600 Grande Ave., Ridgefield, NJ 07657
UI	University of Illinois Film Center (see UIFC below)
UIFC	University of Illinois Film Center, 1325 South Oak St., Champaign, IL 61820 (800) 367-3456
UJ	Unijapan Films, 9-13 Ginza 5-Chome, Chuo-Ku, Tokyo, Japan
UN	University of Nebraska Audio-Visual Instruction, 421 Nebraska Hall, Lincoln, NE 68508 (402) 472-1907
UP	Upjohn Professional Film Library, 7000 Portage Rd., Kalamazoo, MI 49002
USNAC	U.S. Audiovisual Center, General Services Administration, Washington, DC 20409 (301) 763-1896
UT	University of Texas Medical Branch, Galveston, TX 77550 (713) 765-2481
UWF	United World Films, Inc., 221 Park Ave. South, New York, NY 10003
UWM	University of Washington, School of Medicine, Seattle, WA 98105
WNSE	Wards Natural Science Establishment, Inc., P.O. Box 1712, Rochester, NY 14622